				1 **H** 1.00797	2 **He** 4.0026
5 **B** 10.811	6 **C** 12.01115	7 **N** 14.0067	8 **O** 15.9994	9 **F** 18.9984	10 **Ne** 20.183
	14 **Si** 28.086	15 **P** 30.9738	16 **S** 32.064	17 **Cl** 35.453	18 **Ar** 39.948
	32 **Ge** 72.59	33 **As** 74.9216	34 **Se** 78.96	35 **Br** 79.909	36 **Kr** 83.80
		51 **Sb** 121.75	52 **Te** 127.60	53 **I** 126.9044	54 **Xe** 131.30
				85 **At** (210)	86 **Rn** (222)

FOUNDATIONS

OF MODERN

CHEMISTRY

SERIES

The Chemistry

of the

Non-Metals

William L. Jolly

University of California, Berkeley

PRENTICE-HALL, INC., Englewood Cliffs, N.J.

To Jeffrey, Steven, and Jennifer

FOUNDATIONS OF MODERN CHEMISTRY SERIES

Robert W. Parry and Henry Taube, Editors

Current printing (last digit):

10   9   8   7   6   5   4   3   2

Preface

I hope that this book can serve both as an introduction to, and a compendium of, the chemical compounds of the non-metals. Since my main difficulty has been in compressing the material into 144 pages of text, I offer no apologies for using the concise language of practicing chemists. The meanings of many words and expressions that are unfamiliar to a beginning student can be inferred, and the meanings of others can be obtained from other books, when necessary. Certain theoretical concepts (such as molecular orbitals, stereochemistry, the Born-Haber cycle, chain reactions, semiconductor theory, etc.) are very briefly introduced at appropriate places in the text. Throughout, I have tried to strike a reasonable balance in the coverage of structural, kinetic, and thermodynamic data.

I am indebted to many sources, but particularly to W. M. Latimer's *Oxidation Potentials,* 2nd ed. (Prentice-Hall, 1952), which has afforded me many oxidation potential diagrams. The technique of using these diagrams is discussed in Latimer's text and in various other modern textbooks. Also, I have found J. W. Linnett's "double quartet" concept of molecular bonding useful in discussing certain odd molecules and radicals. This concept is discussed in Linnett's *The Electronic Structure of Molecules* (Methuen, 1964) and in the *Journal of the American Chemical Society*, 83 (1961), 2643.

I am grateful to W. A. Benjamin, Inc., for permission to use material from my book, *The Inorganic Chemistry of Nitrogen* (1964). Finally, I wish to thank Professors Henry Taube and Robert Parry for their helpful suggestions.

William L. Jolly

Berkeley, California

Contents

vii

The Chemistry of the Non-Metals

1

Hydrogen

1.1 OCCURRENCE OF HYDROGEN. Spectroscopic analysis of starlight indicates that hydrogen is by far the most abundant element in our galaxy. There are approximately 10 times as many atoms of hydrogen in stellar matter as there are atoms of the next most abundant element, helium. On the other hand, the earth's crust (not including the ice packs, oceans, and atmosphere) contains only about 0.14 percent hydrogen by weight, and dry air contains only about 5×10^{-5} percent by volume of hydrogen. Of course, the ice packs, oceans, lakes, and atmosphere contain vast amounts of hydrogen in the form of water, and all animal and vegetable tissues contain hydrogen.

Many chemists believe that there are more known compounds of carbon than of any other element. However, when one considers the facts that practically all organic compounds contain hydrogen, and that hydrogen forms a multitude of compounds with all the elements except a few of the rare gases, this belief seems questionable. A careful inventory might reveal that there are more known compounds of hydrogen than of any other element.

1.2 THE HYDROGEN ATOM. There are three isotopes of hydrogen, with atomic mass numbers of 1, 2 and 3. The most abundant of these is the isotope of mass 1, and is the isotope generally thought of under the name hydrogen. The isotope of mass 2 is called **deuterium,** and occurs in ordinary hydrogen to the extent of 0.0156 percent. The isotope of mass 3 is called **tritium,** and occurs in ordinary hydrogen to the extent of about 10^{-15} to 10^{-16} percent. It is not usual to give special names to the various isotopes of an element, but the practice is justified in the case of hydrogen because of the appreciably different reactivities of the three isotopes. The different reactivities are a consequence of the very large mass ratios. Deuterium and tritium are discussed in Sec. 1.15 and 1.16. The hydrogen atom consists of a positively charged nucleus (a proton in the case of the mass 1 isotope, and a proton plus one or two neutrons in the case of the other two isotopes) and a negatively charged electron. The atom can exist in any of a large number of energy levels, each characterized by a different set of four quantum numbers. To a first approximation the energy of the atom depends only on the value of the principal quantum number, n. The energy (in volts) of each state, relative to the completely dissociated proton and electron, may be calculated from the relation $E = -13.54/n^2$. A spectral line results from the transition of the atom from one energy level to another.

Ordinarily, hydrogen exists in the form of diatomic molecules, but if sufficient energy (104 kcal/mole) is imparted to the molecules, they will dissociate into atoms. Thus **atomic hydrogen** may be prepared by passing a stream of hydrogen at pressures around 0.5 mm of Hg through an electric discharge. The hydrogen atoms from such a discharge tube have a remarkably long half-life of approximately 0.3 sec. The recombination to form molecular hydrogen is slow because of the difficulty which the atoms have in disposing of the energy which is released upon recombination:

$$2\,H = H_2 \qquad \Delta H^\circ = -104\,\text{kcal/mole}$$

The released energy causes immediate redissociation when it is converted into vibrational energy. (See Fig. 1.1.) Successful recombination is achieved only when the recombining atoms are in contact with a third body, such as an H_2 molecule or the wall of the containing vessel, which can carry off part of the heat of reaction. Such three-body collisions are relatively rare events in ordinary-sized systems at low pressure.

Atomic hydrogen is a very reactive species. It converts most of the elements in the periodic table into their hydrides. The surfaces of metals which do not yield stable hydrides catalyze the recombination reaction and are thereby heated to incandescence. When atomic hydrogen is passed into an aqueous solution, it can dimerize to form molecular hydrogen or react with any oxidizing agent which is present. For example:

$$H + Fe(CN)_6{}^{3-} \longrightarrow H^+ + Fe(CN)_6{}^{4-}$$

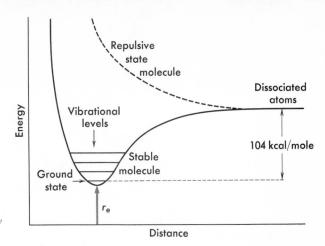

FIGURE 1.1 *Potential energy diagram for H_2 (schematic).*

1.3 MOLECULAR HYDROGEN. Molecular hydrogen, H_2, is the simplest possible molecule. It is composed of four elementary particles: two protons and two electrons. These are held together by electrostatic forces in an assemblage which, like atomic hydrogen, can exist in a number of energy levels. Let us consider the process of bringing together two hydrogen atoms in their ground states. At great distances the energy of the system does not depend on the relative spins of the two electrons. But at distances comparable to the normal bond distance (the distance between the protons in H_2), the relative spins of the electrons are very important. If the spins are aligned such that the electron magnetic moments cancel (antiparallel), the atoms form a stable molecule whose equilibrium distance is indicated by the symbol r_e in Fig. 1.1. If the spins are aligned such that the electron magnetic moments add together (parallel), the atoms form an unstable molecule represented by the upper curve of Fig. 1.1. Repulsions set in at small internuclear distances even for the ground state molecule because electrons resist being crowded into a small space and because strong coulombic repulsions between the protons set in.

1.4 PREPARATION AND USES OF HYDROGEN. Large amounts of hydrogen are manufactured industrially by the catalytic "steam-hydrocarbon" process. This process is based on the following type reactions:

$$C_nH_{2n+2} + nH_2O \longrightarrow nCO + (2n + 1)H_2$$
$$C_nH_{2n+2} + 2nH_2O \longrightarrow nCO_2 + (3n + 1)H_2$$

Another important process for producing hydrogen is the reduction of water vapor by red-hot coke (the water gas reaction):

$$H_2O + C \longrightarrow CO + H_2$$

and the further reaction

$$H_2O + CO \longrightarrow H_2 + CO_2$$

Less important hydrogen-producing reactions are the catalytic cracking of hydrocarbons to improve the octane numbers

$$8\,CH_4 \longrightarrow C_8H_{18} + 7\,H_2$$

and
$$C_6H_{14} \longrightarrow C_6H_6 + 4\,H_2$$

and the electrolysis of aqueous solutions

$$H_2O + e^- \longrightarrow \tfrac{1}{2}\,H_2 + OH^-$$

The latter reaction is involved in the electrolysis of brine to produce sodium hydroxide.

In the laboratory, hydrogen is sometimes made by the action of a dilute solution of H_2SO_4 or HCl on an active metal like zinc. Such hydrogen usually contains traces of volatile hydrides such as AsH_3 and PH_3 resulting from impurities in the metal. These volatile impurities may be removed by bubbling the gas through a solution of a strong oxidizing agent like potassium permanganate.

The most important industrial uses of hydrogen are in catalytic hydrogenation processes. In the Haber process, nitrogen and hydrogen are combined to form ammonia. Methanol is produced by the reaction of carbon monoxide and hydrogen. Unsaturated vegetable oils, such as cottonseed oil, are hydrogenated to saturated, solid fats.

1.5 PHYSICAL PROPERTIES OF HYDROGEN. Some of the important physical properties of hydrogen and deuterium are listed in Table 1.1. The extremely low melting and boiling points of hydrogen indicate that the forces of attraction between the molecules are very weak. Another indication of weak attractive forces is the fact that the temperature of the gas rises when it expands from a high pressure to a low pressure at room temperature. Most gases, for which the intermolecular attractive forces exceed the repulsive forces at room temperature, cool upon expansion at room temperature. Hydrogen gas too, at temperatures below $-68.6°$, cools upon

Table 1.1   SOME PHYSICAL PROPERTIES OF H_2 AND D_2

Physical Property	H_2	D_2
Melting point	$-259.20°$	$-254.43°$
Heat of fusion, cal/mole	28	47
Density of liquid	0.07099	0.1630
	$(-252.78°)$	$(-249.75°)$
Boiling point	$-252.77°$	$-249.49°$
Heat of vaporization, cal/mole	216	293
Critical temperature	$-240.0°$	$-234.8°$
Critical pressure, atm	13.0	16.4
Heat of dissociation at 25°, kcal/mole	104.18	105.96

expansion. In fact, at temperatures lower than that of liquid nitrogen ($-196°$), the cooling effect is great enough to aid in cooling the hydrogen to its liquefaction point.

1.6 THE PROTON MAGNETIC MOMENT. The proton has more than mass and a unit of electrical charge. As a consequence of its spinning motion it also has angular momentum. A spinning charge has a magnetic moment associated with it, and so the proton has a magnetic moment. The proton magnetic moment is of importance to chemists in many phenomena, only two of which (ortho-para hydrogen and proton magnetic resonance) will be discussed here.

Two types of molecular hydrogen, called *ortho* and *para,* are possible. In **ortho hydrogen** the nuclear spins are aligned parallel; in **para hydrogen** the spins are antiparallel. At room temperature and above, hydrogen which has its ortho and para forms at equilibrium contains 75 percent ortho hydrogen and 25 percent para hydrogen. If the temperature is lowered in the absence of catalysts, the ortho-para composition will remain constant. However, in the presence of catalysts such as activated charcoal, or of paramagnetic substances, reequilibration takes place, and the percentage of para hydrogen approaches 100 percent as the temperature approaches 0° K. Thus at 20.39° K the percentage of para hydrogen at equilibrium is 99.79 percent. The ortho and para forms of hydrogen have slightly different physical properties. Thus the melting point of para hydrogen is 0.10 degree lower than that of a 3 : 1 mixture of ortho and para hydrogen. At 20.39° K, the vapor pressure of equilibrated hydrogen is 786.8 mm of Hg, whereas the vapor pressure of the 3 : 1 ortho-para mixture is 760 mm of Hg. Ortho and para hydrogen can be separated from one another by low-temperature gas chromatography, a process in which species are separated on the basis of differing volatilities.

A proton precesses in an externally applied magnetic field in much the same way that a spinning top precesses in a gravitational field. The frequency at which a particular proton precesses depends on the strength of the external magnetic field and upon the local electrical environment of the proton. If we irradiate a hydrogen-containing compound with electromagnetic waves of a particular frequency, a resonance absorption (corresponding to a flipping of the magnetic moments) will occur at a particular magnetic field strength for each structurally distinguishable type of proton in the sample. This is called *proton magnetic resonance,* a type of nuclear magnetic resonance. A proton magnetic resonance spectrum (a plot of the absorption of radiation energy as a function of magnetic field strength) for ethyl alcohol, $CH_3—CH_2—OH$, is given in Fig. 1.2. Each absorption band corresponds to one of the three types of hydrogen atoms in the molecule. It is easy to assign the types of hydrogen atoms to the peaks because the areas under the peaks are proportional to the number of hydrogen atoms of each kind. The fine-structure, or splitting, of the bands is due to the interaction of the proton magnetic moments among themselves. It is not difficult to understand why nuclear magnetic resonance is an extremely valuable tool for chemists.

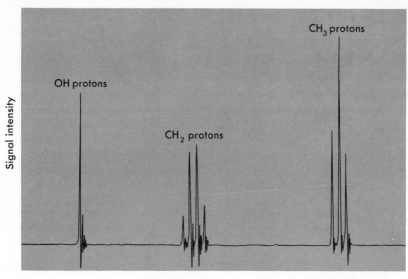

FIGURE 1.2 *Proton magnetic resonance spectrum of ethanol.*

1.7 REACTIONS OF HYDROGEN. Hydrogen is capable of reacting with a large number of elements and compounds, but at room temperature the reactions usually proceed at negligible rates because hydrogen is a relatively inert gas. This inertness is related to the very high dissociation energy of the molecule. Obviously, when an H_2 molecule reacts, the H—H bond must be broken. However, it must not be thought that it is necessary to supply the entire 104 kcal/mole of the dissociation energy. Generally, when an H_2 molecule reacts with another species, at least one of the H atoms forms a bond to another atom at the same time as its bond to the other H atom is broken. Thus the bond-breaking energy is partly compensated for by the bond-forming energy.

Consider the reaction of hydrogen with bromine vapor. The reaction rate is negligible in the absence of light (which catalyzes the reaction) unless the temperature is raised to 200–300°. The initial step in the reaction is the dissociation of bromine to give bromine atoms (53.4 kcal/mole). These Br atoms react with H_2 molecules to give HBr molecules and H atoms, and the latter species react with both Br_2 and HBr molecules. The overall process can be represented by the following steps:

$$Br_2 \longrightarrow 2\,Br \tag{1}$$

$$Br + H_2 \longrightarrow HBr + H \tag{2}$$

$$H + Br_2 \longrightarrow HBr + Br \tag{3}$$

$$H + HBr \longrightarrow H_2 + Br \tag{4}$$

$$2\,Br \longrightarrow Br_2 \tag{5}$$

Notice that the net sum of reactions (2) and (3) is

$$H_2 + Br_2 \longrightarrow 2\,HBr$$

Because of this and the fact that reaction (5) is slow, the number of Br_2 molecules undergoing net reaction with hydrogen is much greater than the number dissociating by reaction (1). Thus we have a *chain reaction* in which the "chain carriers" are H and Br atoms. The reaction proceeds at an appreciable rate even though the concentrations of H and Br atoms are very low. Notice that in this mechanism there is no step corresponding to the simple dissociation of H_2.

Reactions of hydrogen can often be accelerated by solid catalysts, as well as by raising the temperature. These catalysts generally are materials which activate hydrogen by adsorbing it on their surfaces. However, there are a few reactions of molecular hydrogen which proceed at measurable rates at room temperature in the absence of solid catalysts, and these are interesting because of their rarity.

Hydrogen reacts rapidly with B_2Cl_4 at room temperature to form diborane and boron trichloride:

$$3\,B_2Cl_4 + 3\,H_2 \longrightarrow 4\,BCl_3 + B_2H_6$$

Hydrogen reacts at a slow, but measurable rate with aqueous solutions of silver ion, mercuric ion, and cupric ion to form metallic silver, mercurous ion, and cuprous oxide, respectively. Whereas it is thought that hydridic species of the type AgH and CuH_2 are involved in the reaction with Ag^+ and Cu^{2+}, it is believed that atomic mercury is formed in the reaction with Hg^{2+}. The following mechanism has been suggested for the mercury reaction:

$$Hg^{2+} + H_2 \longrightarrow Hg^0 + 2\,H^+ \quad \text{(slow)}$$
$$Hg^0 + Hg^{2+} \longrightarrow Hg_2^{2+} \quad \text{(fast)}$$

Molecular hydrogen is an exceedingly weak acid in water:

$$H_2 = H^+ + H^- \quad K \approx 10^{-38}$$

Evidence for the acidity of hydrogen is found in the fact that the exchange of hydrogen atoms between deuterium gas and ordinary water is catalyzed by the hydroxide ion. The following mechanism is believed to be involved:

$$D_2 + OH^- \rightleftharpoons D^- + DOH$$
$$D^- + H_2O \longrightarrow HD + OH^-$$

Hydrogen reacts with the salts of acids (which are weaker acids than hydrogen) to form the corresponding hydrides and weak acids. Thus hydrogen reacts with potassium phenyl to form potassium hydride and benzene:

$$K^+C_6H_5^- + H_2 \longrightarrow K^+H^- + C_6H_6$$

1.8 SALINE HYDRIDES. Hydrogen reacts at elevated temperatures with the alkali metals and the alkaline-earth metals heavier than beryllium to form salts, such as LiH and CaH_2, containing the anion H^-.

When molten **lithium hydride** is electrolyzed, lithium metal forms at the cathode, and hydrogen is evolved at the anode. These saline hydrides are very similar in their physical properties to the corresponding fluorides. (The ionic radii of F^- and H^- are 1.36 and 1.40 Å, respectively.) By considering Born-Haber cycles for these compounds, one finds that the factor which is most important in determining their stability is the lattice energy, U. The Born-Haber cycle for an alkali metal hydride is represented by the following diagram:

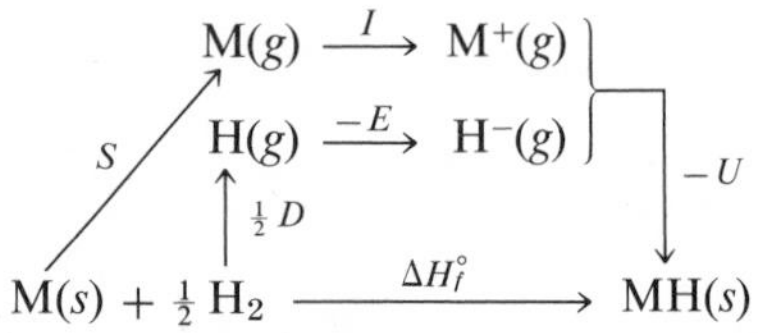

$$
\begin{array}{c}
M(g) \xrightarrow{\;I\;} M^+(g) \\
H(g) \xrightarrow{\;-E\;} H^-(g) \\
\uparrow \tfrac{1}{2}D \\
M(s) + \tfrac{1}{2}H_2 \xrightarrow{\;\Delta H_f^\circ\;} MH(s)
\end{array}
$$

It will be noted that the heat of formation, ΔH_f°, may be broken up into a number of quantities: the sublimation energy of the metal, S; one-half the dissociation energy of hydrogen, $\tfrac{1}{2}D$; the ionization potential of the metal, I; the electron affinity of hydrogen, E, and the lattice energy, U. Thus we may write

$$\Delta H_f^\circ = S + \tfrac{1}{2}D + I - E - U$$

(For these hydrides, ΔH_f° is a negative quantity, corresponding to an exothermic process.) The values for each of these terms for LiH, NaH, and KH are presented in Table 1.2. On going from KH to LiH, the stability (as measured by ΔH_f°) increases. The opposite trend would have

Table 1.2   BORN-HABER FUNCTIONS
FOR ALKALI METAL HYDRIDES (kcal/mole)

	LiH	NaH	KH
ΔH_f°	−21.7	−14.4	−14.2
S	37.1	26.0	21.5
$\tfrac{1}{2}D$	52.1	52.1	52.1
I	123.8	120.0	101.6
E	16.4	16.4	16.4
U	218.3	196.1	173.0

been predicted from the trends in S and I, and it is only because the trend in U more than compensates for these latter trends that the lighter alkali metal hydrides are more stable.

All the saline hydrides react vigorously with protonic solvents such as water, alcohol, and liquid ammonia, to form hydrogen and a base:

$$KH + H_2O \longrightarrow K^+ + OH^- + H_2$$

$$KH + C_2H_5OH \longrightarrow K^+ + C_2H_5O^- + H_2$$

$$KH + NH_3 \longrightarrow K^+ + NH_2^- + H_2$$

Although the hydride ion has never been directly observed in aqueous solutions because of its extreme reactivity, the free energy of the ion has been estimated, permitting us to include the ion in the oxidation potential diagrams for hydrogen.

Acidic Solutions: $\quad H^- \xrightarrow{2.25} H_2 \xrightarrow{0.0} H^+$

Basic Solutions: $\quad H^- \xrightarrow{2.25} H_2 \xrightarrow{0.83} H_2O$

Thus the hydride ion ranks between the metals aluminum and sodium in its reducing power.

1.9 METALLIC HYDRIDES. A number of transition metals and metals of the actinide and lanthanide series absorb hydrogen at elevated temperatures to form solid hydrides. In many cases the metallic lattice undergoes no change other than an expansion in order to accommodate the hydrogen. These hydrides are therefore often called interstitial hydrides. Metallic hydrides usually have rather large composition ranges in which there is no marked change in structure. Thus in **palladium hydride,** the H/Pd ratio may be varied over the range 0.4 to 0.7 without any major change in the structure of the palladium lattice.

It has been observed that hydrogen, when dissolved in wires of palladium, tantalum, titanium, etc., migrates toward the negative end of a potential gradient. This has been interpreted as evidence for the existence of hydrogen as protons in these hydrides. (The electron is presumed to occupy one of the d orbitals of the metal.) However, it may be that only a small fraction of the hydrogen exists in the form of protons. Indeed, the metal-hydrogen bond distances and the salt-like properties of metallic hydrides suggest that the hydrogen is present principally in the form of hydride ions.

1.10 COVALENT HYDRIDES. Compounds containing covalently-bound hydrogen are formed mainly by beryllium, boron, aluminum, gallium, and the elements of Main Groups 4, 5, 6, and 7. The covalent hydrides of the more electropositive of these elements, such as beryllium, boron, and aluminum, react as if the hydrogen atoms had "hydridic" character (that is, act as H^- ions). Thus these hydrides react with water to form hydrogen:

$$B_2H_6 + 6\,H_2O \longrightarrow 6\,H_2 + 2\,H_3BO_3$$

The hydrides of the more electronegative elements such as the halogens and the elements of the oxygen family react as if the hydrogen atoms had protonic character. Thus these hydrides react with bases to form salts or adducts:

$$HCl + NH_3 \longrightarrow NH_4Cl$$

The hydrides of the elements of intermediate electronegativity, such as those of Group 4, show no marked hydridic or protonic character. Depending on the circumstances, such hydrides may show either hydridic or protonic character. Thus germane reacts with hydrogen bromide to form hydrogen

$$GeH_4 + HBr \longrightarrow GeH_3Br + H_2$$

FIGURE 1.3 *The structure of ice, showing the hydrogen bonds. From L. Pauling, The Nature of the Chemical Bond, 3rd ed., p. 465.* © *1960 by Cornell University. Used by permission of Cornell University Press.*

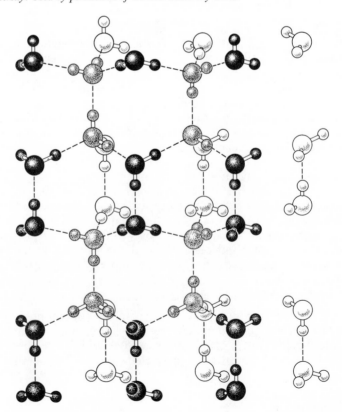

and with sodium amide to form sodium germyl

$$GeH_4 + NaNH_2 \longrightarrow NaGeH_3 + NH_3$$

The chemistry of a number of covalent
hydrides will be discussed under the
chemistries of the principal elements.

1.11 HYDROGEN BONDING. In some
compounds of hydrogen, a hydrogen
atom is bound simultaneously to two
separate electronegative atoms. The
two atoms are said to be *hydrogen
bonded.* The strongest hydrogen bonds
occur between the small, highly electronegative atoms of fluorine, oxygen,
and nitrogen. Thus in the **bifluoride
ion,** HF_2^-, the hydrogen atom forms a
bridge between the two fluorine atoms.
The ion is linear, and the proton is
located midway between the fluoride
ions. In **ice** (see Fig. 1.3) each oxygen
atom is surrounded by four other oxygen atoms, and hydrogen atoms are
located between the oxygen atoms,
although not midway. Each oxygen
atom has two hydrogen atoms at a
distance of 1.01 Å and two hydrogen
atoms at a distance of 1.75 Å, but the
distribution of these bonds throughout the lattice is random. It will be
noticed from Fig. 1.3 that ice has a
rather open structure, with many
holes. When ice melts, some of the
hydrogen bonds are broken, permitting the structure to collapse and causing an increase in density. Hydrogen
bonding is crucial to biology because

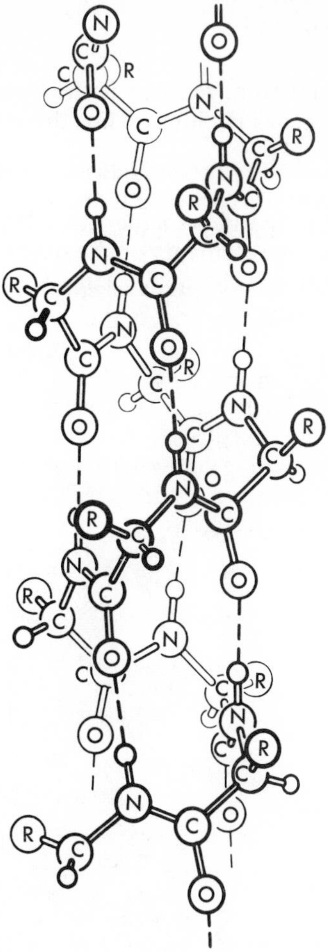

FIGURE 1.4 *The α-helix of polypeptide chains, showing the
N—H ⋯ O hydrogen bonds.
From L. Pauling,* The Nature of
the Chemical Bond, *3rd ed.,
p. 500. © 1960 by Cornell University. Used by permission of
Cornell University Press.*

it plays a major role in determining the configurations of biologically
important molecules. Thus the α-helix configuration of **polypeptide chains**
is held together by N—H⋯O hydrogen bonds. (See Fig. 1.4.)

The compounds **HF, H₂O,** and **NH₃** are strongly hydrogen-bonded in
both the solid and liquid states. (In fact, as a result of hydrogen bonding,
HF is polymeric even in the gaseous state.) Since the processes of melting
and vaporization require the breaking of large numbers of hydrogen bonds
in these hydrogen-bonded compounds, the compounds have abnormally

high heats of melting and vaporization as well as high melting points and boiling points. In Fig. 1.5, the boiling points of a number of covalent hydrides are plotted against the position of the heavy element in the periodic table. It is obvious that the points for HF, H_2O, and NH_3 deviate markedly from the behavior expected for nonassociated liquids.

1.12 THE AQUEOUS PROTON. When a strong acid such as HCl or HNO_3 dissolves in water, the proton dissociates completely from the anion and interacts strongly with the water molecules. It is believed that the proton is very strongly hydrated by one water molecule to form the **oxonium ion,**

FIGURE 1.5 *Boiling points of molecular hydrides and, for comparison, the noble gases.*

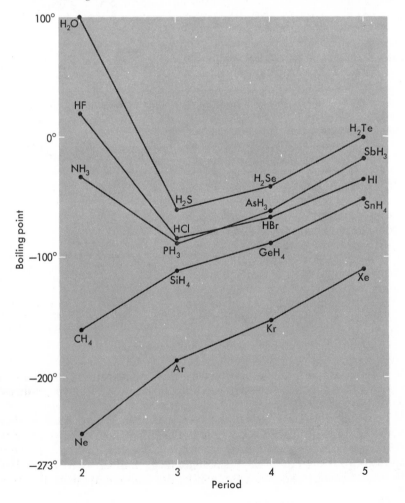

H_3O^+, and that this in turn is fairly strongly hydrogen-bonded to other water molecules, forming species such as $H_9O_4^+$:

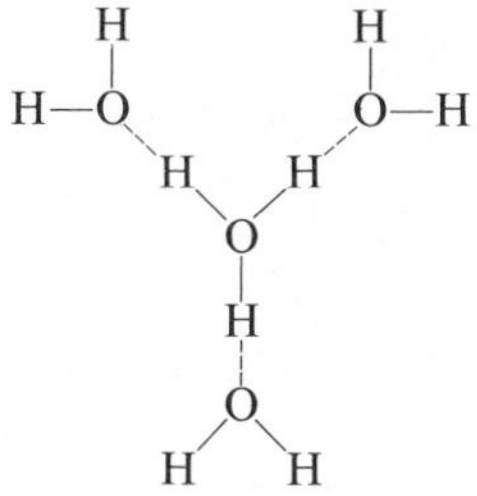

$$
\begin{array}{ccc}
H & & H \\
| & & | \\
H-O & & O-H \\
& H \quad H & \\
& O & \\
& | & \\
& H & \\
& O & \\
& H \quad H &
\end{array}
$$

The peripheral water molecules are, of course, weakly hydrogen-bonded to still other water molecules. In writing chemical equations involving the aqueous proton, we usually do not specify any particular hydrate, but usually represent the aqueous proton by the formula H^+. The oxonium ion, H_3O^+, is pyramidal in shape and exists in various solid acid hydrates such as $HBr \cdot H_2O$ and $H_2SO_4 \cdot H_2O$ (more properly represented as H_3O^+Br and $H_3O^+HSO_4^-$).

It should be noted that, because of its unusual structure, the aqueous proton is a very mobile species. By the slight movement of a few protons in hydrogen bonds, an oxonium ion can in effect move a considerable distance:

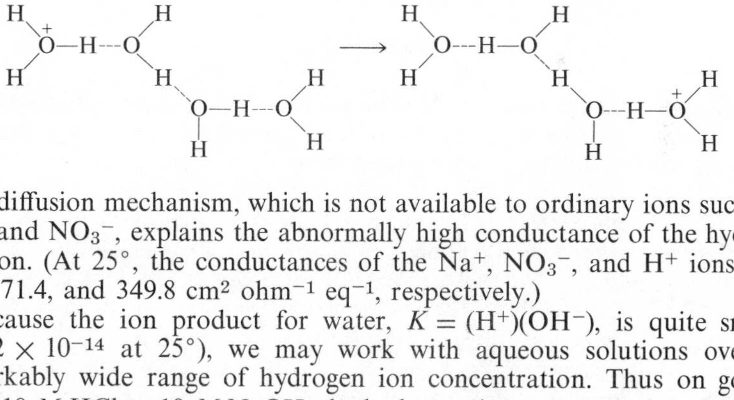

$$\longrightarrow$$

This diffusion mechanism, which is not available to ordinary ions such as Na^+ and NO_3^-, explains the abnormally high conductance of the hydrogen ion. (At $25°$, the conductances of the Na^+, NO_3^-, and H^+ ions are 50.1, 71.4, and 349.8 cm^2 ohm^{-1} eq^{-1}, respectively.)

Because the ion product for water, $K = (H^+)(OH^-)$, is quite small (1.002×10^{-14} at $25°$), we may work with aqueous solutions over a remarkably wide range of hydrogen ion concentration. Thus on going from 10 M HCl to 10 M NaOH, the hydrogen ion concentration changes by a factor of about 10^{16}. It is sometimes convenient to express hydrogen ion concentration in terms of pH, which is defined as $pH = -\log(H^+)$. The hydrogen ion concentrations and pH of several solutions are as follows: for 1 M HCl, $(H^+) = 1$ M and pH = 0; for 0.1 M HCl, $(H^+) = 0.1$ M and pH = 1; for pure water, $(H^+) = 10^{-7}$ M and pH = 7; for 1 M NaOH, $(H^+) = 10^{-14}$ M and pH = 14.

Certain types of glass show an appreciable electric conductivity that is principally due to the mobility of protons in the glass. If we construct a

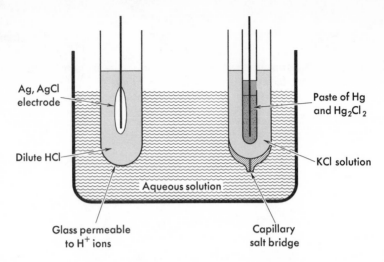

Ag, AgCl electrode

Dilute HCl

Glass permeable to H$^+$ ions

Aqueous solution

Paste of Hg and Hg$_2$Cl$_2$

KCl solution

Capillary salt bridge

FIGURE 1.6   *Glass electrode with calomel (Hg$_2$Cl$_2$) reference electrode for use with pH-meter.*

galvanic cell of the type shown in Fig. 1.6, in which two reference electrodes are separated by a membrane of glass permeable to protons, we find that the emf of the cell changes only when we vary the relative concentrations of the hydrogen ion on opposite sides of the glass membrane. If we keep the hydrogen ion concentration on one side constant, and allow that on the other side to vary, then we observe the relation*

$$E = \text{constant} + 0.059 \log (\text{H}^+)$$

or

$$E = \text{constant} - 0.059 \, \text{pH}$$

where (H$^+$) and pH refer to the solution of variable hydrogen ion concentration. Cells of this type, involving the "glass electrode," form the basis of pH-meters, which are widely used in analytical chemistry.

1.13 AQUEOUS ACIDS.   The binary hydrides of elements on the right-hand side of the periodic table are acidic in aqueous solution. The *pK* values ($-\log \text{K}_{\text{ion}}$) for these hydrides are given in Table 1.3. For most practical purposes, only the hydrides of Groups 6 and 7 show any detectable acidity in water solution. Acids with *pK* values much less than zero are essentially completely ionized at all concentrations. The acidity of a hydride of Group 4, 5, or 6 can be greatly increased by replacing one (or more, when possible) of the hydrogen atoms in the molecule with an atom or group which tends to withdraw electrons from the rest of the molecule. The *pK* values of some compounds which may be looked upon as substitution products of binary hydrides are as follows: (C$_6$H$_5$)$_3$CH, *pK* $\approx$ 32; H$_2$NNO$_2$, *pK* = 7; C$_6$H$_5$SH, *pK* = 8. By far the most important family of acids in aqueous solutions are the **oxy acids,** which may be thought of

---

* Strictly speaking, we should use hydrogen ion *activities* rather than concentrations, but we may usually consider the two to be interchangeable to a fair approximation.

Table 1.3   APPROXIMATE pK VALUES OF SOME BINARY HYDRIDES
IN AQUEOUS SOLUTIONS

Group 4		Group 5		Group 6		Group 7	
CH_4	> 60	NH_3	39	H_2O	16*	HF	3
SiH_4	~ 35	PH_3	27	H_2S	7	HCl	−7
				H_2Se	4	HBr	−9
				H_2Te	3	HI	−10

* Calculated using the 1 molar solution as the standard state for water. Thus $10^{-14}/55.5 \approx 10^{-16}$.

as partially substituted water molecules. It has been found convenient to classify these acids into groups according to the formal charge on the atom to which the —OH group is attached. When the formal charge on this atom is zero, as in H—O—Cl, the pK value is about 8. When the formal charge is +1, as in

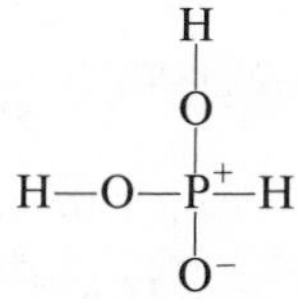

$$
\begin{array}{c}
H \\
| \\
O \\
| \\
H{-}O{-}\overset{+}{P}{-}H \\
| \\
O^-
\end{array}
$$

the pK value is about 3. When the formal charge is +2, as in

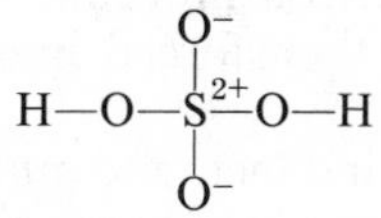

$$
\begin{array}{c}
O^- \\
| \\
H{-}O{-}\overset{2+}{S}{-}O{-}H \\
| \\
O^-
\end{array}
$$

the pK is about −2. When the formal charge is +3, as in

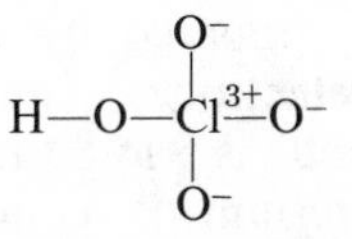

$$
\begin{array}{c}
O^- \\
| \\
H{-}O{-}\overset{3+}{Cl}{-}O^- \\
| \\
O^-
\end{array}
$$

the pK is about −7. In the case of di- and tribasic acids (for example, H_3PO_3 and H_3PO_4, respectively) the successive ionization constants decrease by a factor of approximately 10^{-5}. The pK values for some oxy acids are given in Table 1.4.

1.14 ANALYSIS FOR HYDROGEN.   The hydrogen content of a substance is usually determined by completely oxidizing the substance in a stream of oxygen, and then passing the stream of oxygen through a previously weighed gas absorption tube containing an efficient desiccant such as magnesium perchlorate. The water formed as a result of the oxidation of the hydrogen-containing substance is absorbed by the desiccant and then weighed by difference. Hydrogen or hydrogen compounds in a gaseous

Table 1.4 pK VALUES FOR SOME OXY ACIDS

Formal Charge 0		Formal Charge +1			Formal Charge +2		Formal Charge +3
pK_1	pK_2	pK_1	pK_2	pK_3	pK_1	pK_2	pK
$HOCH_3$ ~16		H_2CO_3* 3.6†	10.3		HNO_3*	<0	$HClO_4$ ≪0
HOH 16		HNO_2* 3.2			H_2SO_4	<0 1.9	$HMnO_4$ ≪0
		H_2TeO_3 2.7	8.0		H_2SeO_4	<0 2.0	
HOI 11.0		H_2SeO_3 2.6	8.3				
H_3AsO_3 9.2		H_3AsO_4 2.3	7.0	13.0			
H_6TeO_6 8.8		H_3PO_4 2.2	7.1	12.3			
HOBr 8.7		$HClO_2$ 2.0					
H_4GeO_4 8.6	12.7	H_3PO_2 2.0					
HOCl 7.2		H_2SO_3** 1.9	7.0				
		H_3PO_3 1.8	6.2				
		H_5IO_6 1.6	6.0				

* Formal charge calculated for structure in which central atom lacks octet.
† Corrected for the unhydrated CO_2.
** See Sec. 6.4.

mixture may be oxidized by hot copper oxide to water, which can then be weighed:

$$CuO + H_2 \longrightarrow Cu + H_2O$$

$$4\,CuO + CH_4 \longrightarrow 4\,Cu + 2\,H_2O + CO_2$$

If it is desired to measure the hydrogen as the gas, the water vapor may be passed over uranium metal at 700°, forming uranium oxide and molecular hydrogen. The hydrogen is then forced into a gas buret and measured.

1.15 DEUTERIUM. The abundance and nuclear structure of deuterium are discussed in Sec. 1.2. Some physical properties of molecular deuterium are presented in Table 1.1, where they may be compared with those of ordinary hydrogen.

Pure deuterium was first prepared by the prolonged electrolysis of 0.5 M NaOH, using nickel electrodes. The fraction of deuterium in the hydrogen evolved at the cathode is 5 to 8 times less than that in the water, and consequently the deuterium is concentrated in the electrolyte. Deuterium is also concentrated by the fractional distillation of water and liquid hydrogen (deuterium concentrates in the residues) and by various exchange reactions such as the following:

$$H_2O(g) + HD(g) = HDO(g) + H_2(g)$$

$$HDO(g) + H_2S(g) = HDS(g) + H_2O(g)$$

Deuterium exchange reactions often yield information regarding the relative reactivities of structurally different hydrogen atoms in molecules. For example, when methylammonium chloride is dissolved in a large amount of heavy water (D_2O) and then isolated by evaporation of the solvent, it is found that only about half the hydrogen in the compound (that bonded to the nitrogen atom) has been replaced by deuterium:

Table 1.5   TRITIUM CONTENTS OF SOME WATER SAMPLES

Water Source	$(T/H) \times 10^{18}$
Precipitation, Chicago	5.5
Precipitation, Honolulu	0.6
Lake Michigan	1.5
Pacific Ocean, Santa Monica	0.5
14-year-old cistern water, Illinois	2.9
2-year-old wine	3.4
24-year-old wine	1.1

$$CH_3NH_3^+ + 3\,D_2O = CH_3ND_3^+ + 3\,HDO$$

The protons on the nitrogen atom are acidic enough to undergo exchange with the solvent protons; the methyl protons show no acidic character in aqueous solution and do not exchange with the solvent.

1.16 TRITIUM.   Tritium is formed continuously in the upper atmosphere by cosmic-ray-induced nuclear reactions. Cosmic rays consist mainly of high-energy protons. These react with nitrogen atoms to form neutrons, and the neutrons in turn react with more nitrogen atoms to form tritium:

$$_7N^{14}(p,n)_8O^{14}, \qquad _7N^{14}(n,_1H^3)_6C^{12}$$

This naturally formed tritium ends up in the form of water and reaches the surface of the earth in rain. Tritium has a half life of 12.5 years with respect to a decay which yields a very soft (0.018 Mev) β^- particle and a $_2He^3$ nucleus. The radioactive decay of tritium is the source of the traces of He^3 in the atmosphere. When a sample of water is stored, it gradually loses its tritium because of the radioactive decay. Chemists have utilized this decay in studies of the circulation of water among oceans, the atmosphere, rivers, and lakes. In Table 1.5, the T/H ratios for various samples of water are listed. The reader is left the puzzle of rationalizing the data.

Tritium is made artificially in nuclear reactors by the reaction of thermal neutrons with lithium: $_3Li^6(n,\alpha)_1T^3$.

SUGGESTED REFERENCES

Bell, R. P., *The Proton in Chemistry*. Ithaca, N.Y.: Cornell University Press, 1959.

Gibb, T. R. P., Jr., "Primary Solid Hydrides," in Vol. 3 of *Progress in Inorganic Chemistry*, F. A. Cotton, ed. New York: Interscience, 1962.

Hurd, D. T., *An Introduction to the Chemistry of the Hydrides*. New York: Wiley, 1952.

Kaufman, S. and W. F. Libby, "The Natural Distribution of Tritium," *Phys. Rev.*, 93 (1954), 1337.

Pimentel, G. C. and A. L. McClellan, *The Hydrogen Bond.* San Francisco: Freeman, 1959.

Roberts, J. D., *Nuclear Magnetic Resonance: Applications to Organic Chemistry*. New York: McGraw-Hill, 1959.

2

The Noble Gases

2.1 ELECTRONIC STRUCTURE. The noble gases **helium, neon, argon, krypton, xenon,** and **radon** constitute Group 0 of the Periodic Table. Except for helium, these elements are characterized by electronic configurations completed by a subshell of six *p* electrons. In the case of helium the first quantum group is complete with only two electrons. Inasmuch as an electron does not shield a full unit of nuclear charge from other electrons having the same values of the *n* and *l* quantum numbers, the outermost electrons of a noble gas are held tightly by a high effective nuclear charge. Consequently the noble gases have high ionization potentials (see Table 2.1), and are almost chemically inert.

Because of the relative stability of a completed *p* shell of electrons, many other elements form compounds in which the atoms have, by the appropriate loss or gain of electrons, achieved noble gas electronic configurations. Some ions which are isoelectronic with noble gases are listed in Table 2.1. This concept of the stable noble gas configuration is useful in systematizing and predicting the structures of the transition metal carbonyls. In almost all metal carbonyls, the metal atoms may be considered to have noble gas electronic configurations if we assume that every CO group contributes two electrons to the outer orbitals of a metal atom. Thus the metal atoms in $Ni(CO)_4$ and $Mo(CO)_6$ have achieved the electronic configurations of krypton and xenon, respectively. In $Co_2(CO)_8$ and $Mn_2(CO)_{10}$, noble gas configurations are achieved by metal-metal bonding as well as by coordination of carbon monoxide.

2.2 DISCOVERY, OCCURRENCE, AND PREPARATION.   In 1784, Cavendish sparked mixtures of air and oxygen, absorbing the resulting nitrogen dioxide in aqueous alkali. When no further volume reduction took place on sparking, he removed the excess oxygen by burning sulfur, and absorbed the sulfur dioxide in aqueous alkali. He always was left with a small residue of unreactive gas. The significance of these experiments was not recognized until more than a century later. In 1892, Rayleigh found that nitrogen prepared from pure ammonia was always less dense by about 0.5 percent than the gas obtained from air by removal of oxygen, carbon dioxide, and water. Rayleigh's contemporary, Ramsay, believed that the discrepancy was caused by the presence of a heavy, unreactive gas in air. Rayleigh and Ramsay then showed that the gas remaining after the removal of all the known constituents of air had an emission spectrum different from that of any known element. The new gas was named **argon.** Before the turn of the century Ramsay and his assistant, Travers, had discovered **neon, krypton,** and **xenon** by the fractional distillation of liquid air.

In 1868, Lockyer observed a yellow line in the spectrum of the sun which did not appear in the spectrum of any element known on the earth at that time. The new element was named **helium,** from the Greek word *helios,* meaning "sun." About 20 years later, Hillebrand observed that when a particular uranium mineral was treated with acid, an unreactive gas, which he thought was nitrogen, was evolved. In 1895, Ramsay repeated Hillebrand's work and showed spectroscopically that the inert gas was the same as Lockyer's helium.

In 1900, several investigators independently observed that a radioactive gas is given off by the elements thorium and radium. Soddy proved that the

Table 2.1   THE NOBLE GASES AND IONS
WITH NOBLE GAS CONFIGURATIONS

Noble Gas	Atomic Number	Ionization Potential (electron volts)	Isoelectronic Ions
He	2	24.586	H^-, Li^+, Be^{2+}
Ne	10	21.563	O^{2-}, F^-, Na^+, Mg^{2+}, Al^{3+}
Ar	18	15.759	S^{2-}, Cl^-, K^+, Ca^{2+}, Sc^{3+}
Kr	36	13.999	Se^{2-}, Br^-, Rb^+, Sr^{2+}, Y^{3+}
Xe	54	12.129	Te^{2-}, I^-, Cs^+, Ba^{2+}, La^{3+}
Rn	86	10.747	At^-, Fr^+

gas, **radon,** was a member of the noble gas family by demonstrating its chemical inertness toward various reagents.

Helium, which originates from the α-decay of heavy radioactive elements, is found to the extent of a few percent in the natural gas from certain wells in the southwestern United States. Only the Bureau of Mines produces helium in the United States. The other noble gases, except radon, are produced by fractional distillation of liquid air. The proportions of the noble gases in air are, in parts per million by volume: He, 5.24; Ne, 18.2; Ar, 9340; Kr, 1.14; Xe, 0.08; and Rn, 6×10^{-14}. The principal isotope of argon, Ar^{40}, is a product of the β-decay of potassium-40, and this decay accounts for the large abundance of argon.

2.3 PHYSICAL PROPERTIES. The more important physical properties of the noble gases are given in Table 2.2. The low melting points, boiling points, and heats of vaporization all indicate that only weak Van der Waals forces are involved in holding the atoms together in the condensed state.

Helium is the lowest-boiling substance known, and is so unique in its behavior as a liquid that it deserves special mention. A somewhat distorted diagram of state for helium of mass 4 is presented in Fig. 2.1. It will be noted that at no point can helium-4 exist with all three phases (liquid, solid, and gas) in equilibrium. The liquid remains in equilibrium with the vapor all the way down to 0° K. To solidify helium at 0° K a pressure of approximately 25 atm must be applied. When liquid helium is cooled below the λ-line (Fig. 2.1), it changes from the relatively normal liquid, **helium I,** to the very unusual **helium II.** Helium II possesses, among other strange properties, "superfluidity," or zero viscosity, and a very high heat conductivity.

The diagram for helium-3 (which exists in ordinary helium to the extent of only a part in a million) is similar to that for helium-4; however, there is no λ-line, and the melting point curve shows a minimum at 29.3 atm and 0.32° K.

Table 2.2   PHYSICAL PROPERTIES OF THE NOBLE GASES

	He	Ne	Ar	Kr	Xe	Rn
Melting point, °C	−272.2 (25 atm)	−248.6	−189.4	−157.2	−111.8	−71
Boiling point, °C	−268.9	−246.1	−185.9	−153.4	−108.1	−62
Heat of vaporization at bp, cal/mole	19.4	414	1558	2158	3020	4325
Critical pressure, atm	2.26	26.9	48.3	54.3	57.6	62
Critical temperature, °C	−267.9	−228.7	−122.3	−63.8	16.6	105
Density of liquid at bp	0.125	1.207	1.400	2.413	3.057	4.4
Solubility in water at 1 atm partial pressure, 20° C, cc (STP) per liter	8.61	10.5	33.6	59.4	108.1	230
Color of light emitted by discharge tube containing gas	yellow	red	red or blue	yellow-green	blue-green	—

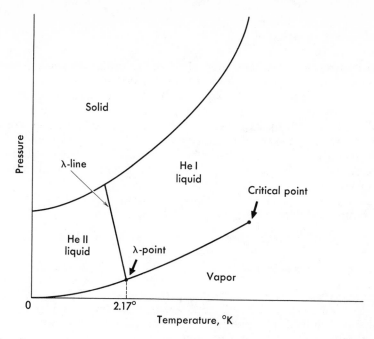

FIGURE 2.1 *Schematic diagram of state for helium-4.*

2.4 CHEMICAL PROPERTIES. It has been known for many years that the noble gases will react in electric discharges to form a wide variety of diatomic ions such as He_2^+, Ar_2^+, $HeNe^+$, $ArXe^+$, HeH^+, etc. The helium hydride ion, HeH^+, has a remarkably high dissociation energy of approximately 45 kcal/mole.

A number of noble gas "clathrates" are known, in which the noble gas "guest" atoms are held by Van der Waals forces in crystalline "cages" formed by "host" substances. Thus hydrates with the approximate empirical formulas $Ar(H_2O)_6$, $Kr(H_2O)_6$, and $Xe(H_2O)_6$ have been prepared. The dissociation pressures of these compounds at 0° C are 105, 14.5, and 1.5 atm, respectively. Hydroquinone clathrates containing argon (8.8 wt percent) and krypton (15.8 wt percent), and phenol clathrates of the approximate compositions $(C_6H_5OH)_4 \cdot Ar$, $(C_6H_5OH)_4 \cdot Kr$, and $(C_6H_5OH)_3Xe$ have been prepared.

In 1962, Bartlett and Lohmann of the University of British Columbia reported that platinum hexafluoride reacts with molecular oxygen in a 1:1 molar ratio to form an orange-red solid. They found the crystal structure and magnetic properties of the solid to be consistent with the concept that each oxygen molecule loses one of its electrons to a PtF_6 molecule to form an ionic crystal of the type $O_2^+[PtF_6^-]$. Because the first ionization potential of molecular oxygen, 12.08 ev, is about the same as that of xenon, Bartlett reasoned that xenon should form a similar compound with platinum hexafluoride, and he experimentally verified his prediction by preparing the yellow compound $XePtF_6$. This simple but dramatic experiment completely invalidated the commonly held view that

21

the noble gases were incapable of forming normal chemical compounds. Shortly after the publication of the discovery of xenon hexafluoro-platinate, chemists at the Argonne National Laboratory near Chicago showed that fluorine and xenon react at 400° to form a volatile, colorless solid, **xenon tetrafluoride,** XeF_4. Soon chemists all over the world were studying the reactions of noble gases and noble-gas compounds. Some of the xenon compounds which have been prepared are listed in Table 2.3. In addition to these compounds, fluorides of krypton and radon have been prepared.

Approximate values of the aqueous oxidation potentials for xenon are given in the following diagrams.

Acidic Solutions: $Xe \xrightarrow{-1.8} XeO_3 \xrightarrow{-2.3} H_4XeO_6$

Basic Solutions: $Xe \xrightarrow{-0.9} HXeO_4^- \xrightarrow{-0.9} HXeO_6^{3-}$

These potentials are consistent with the observed aqueous chemistry of xenon. Xenon(VI) is stable in aqueous acid, but disproportionates in alkaline solution. The halide ions except fluoride are readily oxidized by Xe(VI) in acid solutions, but only slowly in alkaline solutions. Aqueous xenon(VIII) is unstable, oxygen and Xe(VI) being formed. This decomposition is slow in alkaline solutions (1 percent per hour for a 0.003 M solution at pH 11.5) and rapid in solutions of low pH (greater than 1 percent per minute at pH 8). In dilute acid Xe(VIII) rapidly oxidizes manganous to permanganate. Xenon(VI) is oxidized to Xe(VIII) by ozone in alkaline solutions, but the oxidation of elementary xenon by ozone does not take place, probably because of a very high activation energy.

2.5 USES. Helium gas is used instead of hydrogen for filling balloons and dirigibles because it is non-inflammable and has a lifting power only about 8 percent less than that of hydrogen. Helium is a component of the

Table 2.3   COMPOUNDS OF XENON

	Oxidation State of Xe				
	I	*II*	*IV*	*VI*	*VIII*
Fluorides		XeF_2	XeF_4	XeF_6	
Oxyfluorides				$XeOF_4$	
				XeO_2F_2	
Oxides				XeO_3	XeO_4
Adducts	$XePtF_6$	$Xe(PtF_6)_2$		$XeF_5(AsF_6)$	
probably having				$XeF_5(BF_4)$	
ionic structures	$XeRhF_6$	$Xe(SbF_6)_2$		$CsXeF_7$	
	$XeRuF_6$	$Xe(TaF_6)_2$		Cs_2XeF_8	
				$RbXeF_7$	
	Xe_2SiF_6			Rb_2XeF_8	
Oxy-anions known in solid salts				$XeO_4{}^{2-}$	$XeO_6{}^{4-}$

artificial atmosphere supplied to men engaged in deep diving and caisson operations because helium is much less soluble in blood than is nitrogen. (The time required to reduce the pressure to atmospheric without causing the "bends" is greatly reduced by replacing the nitrogen of air with helium.) Helium is also used as a diluent for oxygen in asthma therapy when the air passages are constricted. Liquid helium is used as a coolant and heat transfer medium in cryogenic studies in the neighborhood of 0–5° K. Helium gas is used as a heat transfer agent in gas-cooled atomic reactors because it is chemically inert and does not become radioactive. Both helium and argon are used in large amounts in noble-gas-shielded arc-welding processes. The noble gas protects the hot welded metal from oxidation by the air.

When an electric discharge is established in neon gas at low pressures, a bright orange-red glow is produced. This glow is the basis of the principal use of neon today, in the familiar luminous neon sign tubes.

In addition to its use in arc-welding, argon is used in filling incandescent and fluorescent lamps. The presence of the noble gas in incandescent lamps retards the sublimation of the filament and thus both prolongs the life of the lamp and retards its blackening. In fluorescent lamps, argon serves as an ionizable gas for starting the lamp and for carrying the current during its operation. Krypton and xenon are likewise used, but to a much smaller extent, in the filling of fluorescent lamps and other special lamps. Argon is often used in chemical laboratories to provide an inert atmosphere for the handling of substances that are reactive toward water, oxygen, or nitrogen.

2.6 ANALYSIS. The noble gases can be separated from one another and from other gases either by fractional distillation at low temperatures or by gas chromatography. Mass spectroscopy is very useful for the identification and quantitative estimation of noble gases in mixtures.

SUGGESTED REFERENCES

Bartlett, N., "New Compounds of Noble Gases: The Fluorides of Xenon and Radon," *American Scientist*, 51 (1963), 114.

Borst, L. B., "Liquid Helium," *American Scientist*, 52 (1964), 431.

Cook, G. A., ed., *Argon, Helium and the Rare Gases*, Vols. 1 and 2. New York: Interscience, 1961.

Hyman, H. H., ed., *Noble-Gas Compounds*. Chicago: University of Chicago Press, 1963.

3

Fluorine

3.1 THE HALOGEN FAMILY AND THE UNIQUE CHARACTER OF FLUORINE. Although fluorine is a member of the halogen family of elements, its physical and chemical properties are so atypical that we shall discuss its chemistry in this separate chapter. Of course, the other elements of the first period (Li, Be, B, C, N, O) are also atypical members of their respective families, and (except for the metals Li and Be) we shall discuss them in separate chapters also. Most of the peculiar properties of the first-period elements can be explained by the facts that (1) the atoms are small, (2) the electron clouds are tightly held, very compact, and not easily distorted, and (3) no low-lying d orbitals are available for bonding.

The electronic structure of a free halogen atom is the same as that of a noble gas, except that one of the outer p electrons is missing. In view of the stability of a completed p shell (see Sec. 2.1), it is understandable that all halogen atoms have a strong tendency to pick up electrons to form halide ions:

$$e^-_{(g)} + X_{(g)} \longrightarrow X^-_{(g)}$$

The heat liberated in this type of reaction is called the electron affinity of X. The electron affinities of the halogens are given in Table 3.1. It will be noted

24

Table 3.1 SOME PROPERTIES OF THE HALOGENS

Property	F	Cl	Br	I
Electron affinity of X, kcal/mole	79.5	83.3	77.5	70.6
Ionic radius of X^-, Å	1.36	1.81	1.95	2.16
Typical covalent radius, Å	0.64	0.99	1.14	1.33
Ionization potential of X, kcal/mole	401.8	298.86	274.61	240.78
Oxidation potential,				
$\quad 2\,X^- = X_2 + 2\,e$, E^0 (volts)	−2.87	−1.36	−1.07	−0.54
Dissociation energy, kcal/mole, for:				
$\quad$ halogen molecule (X_2)	36.7	57.1	45.5	35.5
$\quad$ monofluoride (XF)		60.3	59.4	66.2
$\quad$ monochloride (XCl)			51.5	49.6
$\quad$ monobromide (XBr)				41.9

that the electron affinities increase on going from I to Br to Cl, but that F is out of line, with an electron affinity close to that of Br.

Another way a halogen atom can achieve an electron configuration approximating that of a rare gas is by sharing a pair of electrons with another halogen atom, thus forming a diatomic molecule. All possible diatomic combinations of the halogens have been observed; the energies required to dissociate them into atoms are listed in Table 3.1. It will be noted that the trend toward higher dissociation energies on going from I_2 to Cl_2 is broken by F_2, the dissociation energy of which is about the same as that of I_2.

Various other physical properties of the halogens are presented in Table 3.1. In most cases the property associated with fluorine is considerably different from what would have been predicted from the other three halogens, assuming a regular family trend. Further evidence of the unique character of fluorine is found in the fact that no oxy acids of fluorine corresponding to HOCl, $HClO_2$, etc., are known. Thus the aqueous chemistry of fluorine is relatively simple.

3.2 OCCURRENCE AND ISOLATION. Fluorine constitutes approximately 0.03 percent of the earth's crust;* it is found principally in the form of **fluorspar,** CaF_2, **cryolite,** Na_3AlF_6, and **fluorapatite,** $Ca_5F(PO_4)_3$.

Hydrogen fluoride is prepared by heating finely-ground fluorspar with concentrated sulfuric acid; an anhydrous product is obtained by fractional distillation of the crude product.

Elementary fluorine was first prepared in 1886 by the French chemist Moissan. He prepared anhydrous hydrogen fluoride by heating the compound **KHF_2**; the HF was condensed directly in a platinum vessel and subjected to electrolysis. From the anode a gas was evolved that set fire to silicon, produced ozone with water, and liberated chlorine from potassium chloride. Moissan communicated his discovery to the Academy of

---

* The "earth's crust" refers to the rocks only, and does not include the atmosphere and oceans.

Sciences, and he was asked to demonstrate the preparation before a special committee. Of course, Moissan made very careful preparations, but on the day of the demonstration he obtained no fluorine—in fact, he was unable to pass any current through the hydrogen fluoride. A few days later he found that the fault lay in the fact that he had doubly distilled the HF for the special demonstration. Previously, entrained KHF_2 had collected in the electrolysis vessel and had provided the solution with the conductivity that pure HF did not have. From then on, he added the salt to the electrolysis vessel and successfully prepared fluorine.

Even today, fluorine is prepared by the electrolysis of concentrated solutions of potassium fluoride in anhydrous hydrogen fluoride. The electrolysis cell is generally made of steel, copper, or Monel metal and is operated at an elevated temperature, such as 100°. If the electrolyte is not absolutely anhydrous, the anode product is contaminated with **oxygen fluoride**, OF_2.

3.3 PHYSICAL AND CHEMICAL PROPERTIES OF FLUORINE. Fluorine melts at $-218.0°$, boils at $-187.9°$, and has a yellow color. The heat of fusion is 372 cal/mole and the heat of vaporization is 1.51 kcal/mole.

Fluorine atoms form very strong bonds to almost all the elements in the periodic table, and yet the F—F bond energy is very low. Consequently, fluorine reacts with all the elements except oxygen and the lighter noble gases to form thermodynamically stable fluorides. Certain metals such as copper can be used to contain elementary fluorine only because protective layers of metal fluoride, which prevent further reaction, form on their surfaces. Fluorine reacts explosively with organic material, forming HF and CF_4. **Teflon** (a $-CF_2-CF_2-$polymer) is inert toward fluorine at ordinary temperatures. Dry glassware can be used in the laboratory to handle fluorine, provided all traces of HF are removed.

Very few species have the oxidizing power of elementary fluorine. The aqueous oxidation potentials

$$2\,F^- = F_2 + 2\,e^- \qquad E^0 = -2.87$$
$$2\,HF = F_2 + 2\,H^+ + 2\,e^- \qquad E^0 = -3.06$$

are not of much significance because fluorine cannot exist in contact with water. It rapidly oxidizes water to oxygen; in alkaline solution, oxygen fluoride is formed.

3.4 SALINE FLUORIDES. Metals with large cations of low charge form saline fluorides—that is, fluorides with three-dimensional ionic lattices. These salts have high melting and boiling points and are electrically conducting in the molten state. The properties of some of these fluorides are given in Table 3.2. It will be noted that the heats of formation of the alkali metal fluorides, like those of the alkali metal hydrides, become more negative on ascending from Cs to Li. The increase in lattice energy on going to the metal ions of smaller size is most important in establishing this trend. (See Sec. 1.8.) However, the opposite trend is found for the alkaline-earth fluorides (save BaF_2); here the metal ions are all small enough, compared to the fluoride ion, that the lattice energy does not increase rapidly on ascending from Sr to Be. In the case of chlorides, bromides, and iodides, the stabilities decrease on ascending either the alkali metal or alkaline-earth families. (See Table 4.4.) The fluorides of lithium, the alkaline-earths, and the rare earths, are only slightly soluble in water. Many cations of small size and high charge form more stable complexes with fluoride ion than they do with the other halide ions. Thus aluminum forms a series of fluoride complexes, AlF^{2+}, AlF_2^+, AlF_3, AlF_4^-, AlF_5^{2-}, and AlF_6^{3-}, whereas it is only very slightly complexed by the other halides. Other examples are the species BF_4^-, SiF_6^{2-}, FeF_6^{3-}, and CoF_6^{3-}. However, some metal ions, such as Hg^{2+} and Ag^+, are more strongly complexed by the heavier halides than by fluoride. In such cases the higher polarizability of the larger halide ions is probably important.

The alkali metal fluorides form hydrogen-bonded acid fluorides of the type $KF \cdot HF$, $KF \cdot 3HF$, and $KF \cdot 4HF$.

It has been shown that children who regularly drink water containing at least 1 part per million of fluoride ion throughout the period when their permanent teeth are growing have fewer cavities than children whose water supply has a much lower concentration of fluoride ion. For this reason, many communities whose water has a low concentration of fluoride ion "fluoridate" their water with soluble fluorides, such as sodium

Table 3.2   PROPERTIES OF SOME SALINE FLUORIDES

Fluoride	Heat of Formation, (kcal/g. atom of F at 25°)	Crystal Structure	Melting Point (°C)	Solubility in Water (g./100 g. sat. soln. at 25°)
LiF	−145.7	NaCl	847	0.133
NaF	−136.3	NaCl	995	3.98
KF	−134.5	NaCl	857	50.4
RbF	−131.8	NaCl	775	75.1 (18°)
CsF	−130.3	NaCl	682	85.4 (18°)
BeF_2	−121	β-cristobalite	797	—
MgF_2	−134	rutile	1263	0.013
CaF_2	−145.1	fluorite	1418	0.002
SrF_2	−145.2	fluorite	1400	0.04
BaF_2	−143.5	fluorite	1353	0.12
AlF_3	−118.8	Coord. No. 6; 2 Al—F distances	> 1270	0.56
CrF_2	−90.5	distorted rutile	1100	low
AgF	−48.5	NaCl	435	64.2

fluoride, to bring the concentration up to 1 part per million. The inclusion of fluoride in tooth paste is also effective in preventing tooth decay; in such preparations it has been found that stannous fluoride is more effective than sodium fluoride. The principal constituent of tooth enamel is **hydroxyapatite,** $Ca_5OH(PO_4)_3$. In the presence of fluoride ion, this is converted to the harder, more acid-resistant **fluorapatite,** $Ca_5F(PO_4)_3$. A water supply can contain too much fluoride, however: concentrations greater than 2 ppm cause some mottling of teeth.

3.5 COVALENT FLUORIDES.

Hydrogen fluoride, HF, is a highly hydrogen-bonded liquid which freezes at $-83.1°$ and boils at $19.9°$. The liquid has a very high dielectric constant (60 at $19°$) and dissolves many inorganic and organic compounds. Even in the vapor state, hydrogen fluoride is hydrogen bonded. At $20°$ and 745 mm., 80 percent of the HF is polymerized in the form of $(HF)_6$. The other hydrogen halides do not show this strange property.

In aqueous solutions HF is a weak acid:

$$HF = H^+ + F^- \qquad K = 6.7 \times 10^{-4}$$

Fluoride ion reacts with HF to form the remarkable bifluoride ion, HF_2^-:

$$F^- + HF = HF_2^- \qquad K = 3.9$$

In this ion, the proton is located midway between the two fluoride ions; the complex is held together largely by electrostatic forces. (See Sec. 1.11.) From the magnitude of the equilibrium constant, it is clear that aqueous solutions of HF contain appreciable concentrations of HF_2^-. Aqueous **hydrofluoric acid** is usually handled in plastic or steel containers because it reacts with glass to form gaseous **silicon tetrafluoride:**

$$SiO_2 + 4\,HF \longrightarrow SiF_4 + 2\,H_2O$$

The nonmetals, and many metals, form molecular fluorides which are usually gases or volatile liquids. The melting points and boiling points of some of these fluorides are given in Table 3.3. The extraordinary volatility of these fluorides is due to the fact that the polarizability of the fluorine atom is very low and that consequently the intermolecular Van der Waals forces are very weak. Because of the low dissociation energy of fluorine, the strong bonds that it forms with other elements, and its small size (permitting high coordination numbers), many elements show their highest oxidation states as fluorides. Some fluorides probably owe their stability to the ability of fluorine to use its filled p orbitals for double bonding to the central atom. Thus **BF₃** is a weaker acid than **BCl₃** because of such stabilization:

Table 3.3 PROPERTIES OF SOME BINARY MOLECULAR FLUORIDES

	Melting Point (°C)	Boiling Point (°C)		Melting Point (°C)	Boiling Point (°C)
XeF_2	140	3.8 mm, 25°	Te_2F_{10}	−34	53
XeF_4	114	3 mm, 25°	NF_3	−206.8	−129.0
XeF_6	46	29 mm, 25°	N_2F_2(cis)	< −195	−105.7
ClF	−155.6	−100.3	N_2F_2(trans)	−172	−111.4
ClF_3	−82.6	12.1	N_2F_4	−168	−73
BrF	−33	20	FN_3	−154	−82
BrF_3	8.8	127.6	PF_3	−151.5	−101.5
BrF_5	−60.5	40.5	PF_5	−93.7	−84.5
IF_5	8.5	97	AsF_3	−5.95	62.8
IF_7	4.5	5.5	AsF_5	−79.8	−53.2
OF_2	−223.8	−145.3	SbF_3	292	319(subl)
O_2F_2	−163.5	−57	SbF_5	8.3	150
O_3F_2	−189	—	BiF_3	725	—
S_2F_2	−165	−10.6	BiF_5	<160	230
SF_4	−121	−40.4	CF_4	−183.7	−182.0
SF_6	−51	−65(subl)	SiF_4	−90.3	−95.5(subl)
S_2F_{10}	−55	29	GeF_4	−15.0	−36.8(subl)
SeF_4	−9.5	106	BF_3	−128.7	−99
SeF_6	−34.6	−46.6(subl)	PtF_6	61.3	69.1
TeF_4	129.6	—	WF_6	2.3	17.1
TeF_6	−37.8	−38.9(subl)			

The extraordinary stability of compounds such as **SiF₄, PF₅** and **SF₆** is probably due to the availability on the central atoms of empty $3d$ orbitals which permit partial double bonding to the fluorine atoms.

Many fluorides can be prepared by direct fluorination of the appropriate element or a lower fluoride:

$$S + 3 F_2 \longrightarrow SF_6$$

$$SbF_3 + F_2 \longrightarrow SbF_5$$

A variety of methods has been used for the conversion of chlorides to fluorides:

$$TiCl_4 + 4 HF\text{(anhydrous)} \longrightarrow TiF_4 + 4 HCl$$

$$PCl_3 + AsF_3 \longrightarrow PF_3 + AsCl_3$$

$$3 SiCl_4 + 4 SbF_3 \xrightarrow{\text{SbCl}_5 \text{ catalyst}} 3 SiF_4 + 4 SbCl_3$$

$$3 SCl_2 + 4 NaF \xrightarrow{\text{refluxing CH}_3\text{CN}} SF_4 + S_2Cl_2 + 4 NaCl$$

$$VCl_3 \xrightarrow{\text{BrF}_3} VF_5$$

Sulfur tetrafluoride has been found to be a very useful fluorinating agent for organic oxygen compounds; for example:

$$\underset{R}{\overset{R}{\diagdown}}C{=}O + SF_4 \longrightarrow \underset{R}{\overset{R}{\diagdown}}CF_2 + SOF_2$$

The hydrogen of many organic compounds and some inorganic compounds can be replaced with fluorine by the electrolysis of the compound in liquid HF. Some of the conversions which have been effected in this way include the preparation of $(C_2F_5)_2O$ from $(C_2H_5)_2O$, the preparation of C_6F_{14} from C_6H_{14}, and the preparation of NF_3 from $NH_4{}^+$.

Pure **bromine trifluoride** is a liquid with a rather high electrical conductivity ($\kappa = 8 \times 10^{-3}$ ohm^{-1} cm^{-1} at 15° for BrF_3, compared with $\kappa = 4 \times 10^{-8}$ ohm^{-1} cm^{-1} at 18° for water). The conductivity is explained by the self-ionization forming $BrF_2{}^+$ and $BrF_4{}^-$ ions. The current is carried by migration of the ions. Bromine trifluoride forms adducts with many metal fluorides. Thus potassium fluoride reacts with BrF_3 to form potassium tetrafluorobromate(III), $KBrF_4$, and antimony pentafluoride reacts to form difluorobromine(III) hexafluoroantimonate(V), BrF_2SbF_6. According to the "solvent" acid-base concept, $KBrF_4$ is a base, and BrF_2SbF_6 is an acid in bromine trifluoride. Thus, when solutions of these reagents in bromine trifluoride are mixed, a neutralization reaction takes place:

$$BrF_2{}^+ + BrF_4{}^- = 2\,BrF_3$$

The shapes of molecular fluorides and fluoro-anions are in some cases rather unusual and are significant because they demonstrate the steric influence of lone pairs of electrons. (Of course this influence is shown by other compounds as well, but a wider variety of examples is found among fluorides.) A lone pair of electrons on a central atom is counted among the peripheral atoms in determining the arrangement of the bonding and nonbonding electron pairs around the central atom. When a central atom has more than one lone pair of electrons, the lone pairs are usually positioned so that they are as far apart as possible. The stereochemistry of various fluorides and other compounds is summarized in Table 3.4. Some of the structures are pictured in Fig. 3.1.

3.6 ANALYSIS. Fluoride may be detected in a sample by warming it with silica in 90 percent sulfuric acid. The evolved SiF_4 gas may be

Table 3.4 STEREOCHEMISTRY OF FLUORIDES AND OTHER HALOGEN COMPOUNDS HAVING FOUR OR MORE PERIPHERAL ELECTRON PAIRS

Peripheral Electron Pairs	Arrangement of Electron Pairs	Ligands	Lone Pairs	Shape of Molecule or Ion	Examples
4	tetrahedron	4	0	tetrahedron	GeF_4, $BF_4{}^-$
		3	1	trigonal pyramid	NF_3, $ClO_3{}^-$
		2	2	V-shaped	OF_2, $ClO_2{}^-$
5	trigonal bipyramid	5	0	trigonal bipyramid	PF_5
		4	1	distorted tetrahedron	SF_4, $IO_2F_2{}^-$
		3	2	T-shaped	ClF_3
		2	3	linear	XeF_2, $ICl_2{}^-$
6	octahedron	6	0	octahedron	SF_6, $IO_6{}^{5-}$
		5	1	square pyramid	BrF_5, IF_5
		4	2	square	XeF_4, $BrF_4{}^-$
7	pentagonal bipyramid	7	0	pentagonal bipyramid	IF_7

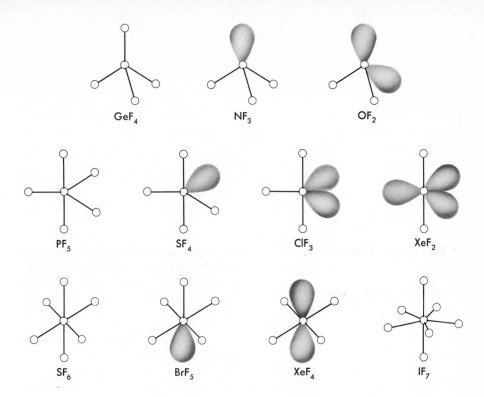

FIGURE 3.1   *Structures of various molecular fluorides (see Table 3.4).*

detected by its formation of turbidity in a drop of water:

$$SiO_2 + 4\,F^- + 4\,H_2SO_4 \longrightarrow SiF_4 + 2\,H_2O + 4\,HSO_4^-$$

$$3\,SiF_4 + 2\,H_2O \longrightarrow SiO_2 + 4\,H^+ + 2\,SiF_6{}^{2-}$$

Fluoride may be quantitatively determined by the precipitation of the sparingly soluble (0.325 g/*l* at 25°) **lead chlorofluoride,** PbClF. The PbClF can be weighed as such, or the volumetric Volhard method (see Sec. 4.10) can be used to determine the chlorine, from which the fluorine can be calculated. Fluoride may also be weighed as **calcium fluoride.** Titrations based on precipitation of rare-earth and thorium fluorides are also used.

SUGGESTED REFERENCES

Gillespie, R. J., "The Valence-Shell Electron-Pair Repulsion Theory of Directed Valency," *J. Chem. Education,* 40 (1963), 295.

Muetterties, E. L., and C. W. Tullock, "Binary Fluorides," Ch. 7 in Vol. 2 of *Preparative Inorganic Reactions,* W. L. Jolly, ed. New York: Interscience, 1965.

Simons, J. H., volumes of *Fluorine Chemistry.* New York: Academic Press, 1950–.

Stacey, M., J. C. Tatlow, and A. G. Sharpe, several volumes of *Advances in Fluorine Chemistry.* London: Butterworth, 1960–.

4

Chlorine, Bromine,

Iodine, and Astatine

4.1 OCCURRENCE AND PREPARATION.
Chlorine, which constitutes about 0.03
percent of the earth's crust, is found
mainly as chloride in sea water, in salt
lakes, and in the deposits formed from
the evaporation of salt lakes. Chlorine
gas is prepared industrially by the
electrolysis of brine:

$$Cl^- + H_2O \longrightarrow \tfrac{1}{2} Cl_2 + \tfrac{1}{2} H_2 + OH^-$$

It is also a by-product of the preparation of metallic sodium, magnesium,
and calcium, in which the appropriate
fused chloride is electrolyzed.

Bromine, constituting about 0.0002
percent of the earth's crust, occurs as
bromide along with, but in smaller
amounts than, chlorine. It is obtained
from sea water by passing chlorine
into it at pH 3.5:

$$Cl_2 + 2 Br^- \longrightarrow Br_2 + 2 Cl^-$$

The bromine is swept out in a current
of air and is absorbed in aqueous carbonate solution:

$$3 Br_2 + 6 CO_3^{2-} + 3 H_2O \longrightarrow$$
$$5 Br^- + BrO_3^- + 6 HCO_3^-$$

By acidification of the solution, the
reaction is reversed, and the bromine
can be distilled out.

Iodine, which makes up about 10^{-4} percent of the earth's crust, is found as iodide in oil-well brines and in the form of iodates in Chilean nitrate deposits. Iodine is liberated from iodates by reduction with limited amounts of bisulfite:

$$2\,IO_3^- + 5\,HSO_3^- \longrightarrow I_2 + 2\,SO_4^{2-} + 3\,HSO_4^- + H_2O$$

The radioactive element **astatine** has been detected in extremely small amounts in the natural decay series of thorium and uranium. The element was first synthesized by bombarding bismuth with high-energy alpha particles: $Bi^{209}(\alpha,2n)At^{211}$.

4.2 PHYSICAL AND CHEMICAL PROPERTIES OF THE ELEMENTS. The important physical properties of chlorine, bromine, and iodine are given in Table 4.1. Aqueous solutions of chlorine and bromine are colored like the corresponding gases. Solutions of iodine in non-basic, unassociated liquids such as carbon tetrachloride, carbon disulfide, and hexane, are violet-colored, like iodine vapor. However, solutions of iodine in liquids whose molecules can donate electrons to the iodine molecule are brownish colored. Water, alcohols, and benzene fall into the latter group of solvents. Iodine forms an intensely blue complex with starch which serves as a delicate test for free iodine.

A characteristic reaction of the halogens is their reaction with olefins (hydrocarbons containing double-bonded carbon atoms):

$$X_2 + \underset{/}{\overset{\backslash}{C}}=\underset{\backslash}{\overset{/}{C}} \longrightarrow X-\overset{|}{\underset{|}{C}}-\overset{|}{\underset{|}{C}}-X$$

These reactions possibly proceed through ionic intermediates in which only one of the two halogen atoms is attached to the olefin. The formation of such intermediates is suggested by the products of brominations carried out in the presence of chloride ion; in such cases a bromochloro compound forms along with the dibromo compound.

4.3 INTERHALOGEN COMPOUNDS AND POLYHALIDES. The dissociation energies of the diatomic halogen halides are given in Table 3.1, and some prop-

Table 4.1 PHYSICAL PROPERTIES OF THE HALOGENS

	Cl_2	Br_2	I_2
Melting point, °C	-101.0	-7.3	113.6
$\Delta H°$ of fusion, kcal/mole	1.53	2.52	3.74
Boiling point, °C	-34.1	58.2	183
$\Delta H°$ of vaporization, kcal/mole	4.88	7.17	9.97
Color of gas	greenish yellow	reddish brown	violet
Solubility in water, M, 20°	0.090 (1 atm)	0.21	1.3×10^{-3}

erties of the halogen fluorides are discussed in Chapter 3. The only known interhalogens of chlorine, bromine, and iodine are **BrCl, ICl, ICl₃** and **IBr.** These compounds are just barely stable with respect to decomposition to the elementary halogens. In fact, the least stable of these compounds, BrCl, has never been isolated in a pure state; it is usually contaminated with bromine and chlorine:

$$BrCl(g) = \tfrac{1}{2} Br_2(g) + \tfrac{1}{2} Cl_2(g) \qquad K_{25°} = 0.33$$

The most stable of these compounds, ICl, is a brownish-red solid of melting point 27.3°.

When certain halides of the larger alkali metals are crystallized in the presence of a halogen or interhalogen, salts containing polyhalide anions are formed. Some examples of these salts are **KI₃, KI₅, KIBrCl, CsICl₄,** and **KBrF₄.** The polyhalide ions which are of importance in aqueous solutions, together with their dissociation constants, are given in Table 4.2.

4.4 SALINE HALIDES. The saline halides are those which consist of infinite lattices of separate metal ions and halide ions in the solid state. The halides of the alkali and alkaline-earth metals (with the exception of beryllium), most of the lanthanides, and the transition metals in their lower oxidation states, are saline in character. The properties of the chlorides of some of these metals are given in Table 4.3.

The more important sparingly soluble halides are those of Ag^+, Hg_2^{2+}, Ti^+, Cu^+, Pb^{2+}, SbO^+, and BiO^+. HgI_2, BiI_3 and SnI_4 are also sparingly soluble. Many metal ions form complex ions with the halides. A few examples are HgI^+, HgI_2, HgI_3^-, HgI_4^-, $InBr^{2+}$, $FeCl^{2+}$, $FeCl_2^+$, $FeCl_3$, and $FeCl_4^-$.

In most saline halides, the number of halide ions coordinated to each metal ion is much greater than the number of halide ions that could be bound to the metal ion in any conceivable discrete molecular configuration. As a rough rule, a halide will crystallize in a molecular lattice only when, in the molecule, the number of halogen atoms bonded to the electropositive atom equals the maximum coordination number of the electropositive atom for that halogen. Molecular halides are characterized by low melting points, and saline halides are characterized by high melting

Table 4.2 DISSOCIATION CONSTANTS OF AQUEOUS POLYHALIDE IONS AT 25°

$I_3^- = I_2(aq) + I^-$	1.32×10^{-3}
$I_2Br^- = I_2(aq) + Br^-$	7.3×10^{-2}
$I_2Cl^- = I_2(aq) + Cl^-$	2.8×10^{-1}
$IBr_2^- = IBr(aq) + Br^-$	2.7×10^{-3}
$ICl_2^- = ICl(aq) + Cl^-$	6×10^{-3}
$Br_3^- = Br_2(aq) + Br^-$	5.9×10^{-2}
$Cl_3^- = Cl_2(aq) + Cl^-$	5.5

Table 4.3 PROPERTIES OF SOME SALINE CHLORIDES

Chloride	Heat of Formation (kcal/g. atom of Cl at 25°)	Crystal Structure	Melting Point (°C)	Solubility in Water (g./100 g. sat. soln. at 25°)
LiCl	−96	NaCl	610	45.85
NaCl	−98.2	NaCl	808	26.43
KCl	−104.18	NaCl	772	26.2
RbCl	−105.1	NaCl	717	48.5
CsCl	−106.3	CsCl	645	65.8
$MgCl_2$	−76.6	$CdCl_2$	714	35.36
$CaCl_2$	−95.0	deformed rutile	782	45.3
$SrCl_2$	−98.9	fluorite	875	35.8
$BaCl_2$	−102.7	$PbCl_2$	962	27.1
$CrCl_2$	−49	—	815	sol.
AgCl	−30.36	NaCl	455	2.26×10^{-4}

points. As the charge/radius ratio of the electropositive atom increases, the probability of forming a molecular halide increases. Thus **NaBr** and **MgBr₂** (melting points 755 and 700°, respectively) form ionic lattices, whereas **Al₂Br₆** and **SiBr₄** (melting points 97.5 and 5°, respectively) form molecular lattices. It is clear that, as the oxidation state of a given metal increases, the molecular character should increase. Thus **SnCl₂** melts at 227° and **SnCl₄** melts at −33.3°.

4.5 COVALENT HALIDES. The important physical properties of **HCl, HBr,** and **HI** are presented in Table 4.4. In aqueous solutions, these acids are completely ionized and cannot be differentiated by their acid strengths. However, in an acidic solvent like acetic acid, these acids are weak and their acidities can be compared. The dissociation constants for HCl and HBr in acetic acid are 5×10^{-10} and 2×10^{-7}, respectively. The decrease

Table 4.4 SOME PROPERTIES OF HCl, HBr, AND HI

	HCl	HBr	HI
Melting point, °C	−114.22	−86.82	−50.80
Boiling point, °C	−85.05	−66.73	−35.36
Dissociation energy, kcal/mole	103.2	87.5	71.4
Heat of solution in an infinite amount of water, $\Delta H°$, kcal/mole, 25°	−17.96	−20.24	−19.57
Concentration of constant-boiling aqueous solution at 1 atm, wt percent	20.24	47	57
Concentration of usual commercial reagent, wt percent:	37	48	47
molarity:	12	9	5.5

in acid strength on going from the heavier hydrogen halides to the lighter hydrogen halides is principally due to the marked increase in the H—X bond energy (see Table 4.4) on ascending this series.

The properties of some molecular chlorides, bromides, and iodides are given in Table 4.5.

4.6 AQUEOUS OXIDATION POTENTIALS. The aqueous oxidation potential diagrams for chlorine, bromine, and iodine in acidic and basic solutions are given below. The X^--X_2 potentials are very important landmarks among oxidation potentials; it is often convenient to classify oxidizing agents as to the halides which they are capable of oxidizing and to classify reducing agents as to the halogens which they are capable of reducing. The increase in oxidizing power on going from I_2 to Br_2 to Cl_2 is largely due to the increase in hydration energy on going from I^- to Br^- to Cl^- (approximately 72, 81, and 89 kcal/mole, respectively) and to the increase in electron affinity on going from I to Br to Cl (see Table 3.1). These factors outweigh the effect of the increase in dissociation energy on going from I_2 to Br_2 to Cl_2 (Table 3.1).

Acidic Solutions:

$$Cl^- \xrightarrow{-1.36} Cl_2 \xrightarrow{-1.63} HOCl \xrightarrow{-1.64} HClO_2 \xrightarrow{-1.21} ClO_3^- \xrightarrow{-1.19} ClO_4^-$$

with -1.47 bridging Cl_2 to ClO_3^-

$$Br^- \xrightarrow{-1.07} Br_2 \xrightarrow{-1.59} HOBr \xrightarrow{-1.49} BrO_3^-$$

with -1.51 bridging Br_2 to BrO_3^-

$$I^- \xrightarrow{-0.54} I_2 \xrightarrow{-1.45} HOI \xrightarrow{-1.14} IO_3^- \xrightarrow{-1.7} H_5IO_6$$

$I_2 \xrightarrow{-1.06} ICl_2^- \xrightarrow{-1.23}$, with -1.20 bridging

Basic Solutions:

$$Cl^- \xrightarrow{-1.36} Cl_2 \xrightarrow{-0.40} ClO^- \xrightarrow{-0.66} ClO_2^- \xrightarrow{-0.33} ClO_3^- \xrightarrow{-0.36} ClO_4^-$$

with -0.88 and -0.50

$$Br^- \xrightarrow{-1.07} Br_2 \xrightarrow{-0.45} BrO^- \xrightarrow{-0.54} BrO_3^-$$

with -0.76

$$I^- \xrightarrow{-0.54} I_2 \xrightarrow{-0.45} IO^- \xrightarrow{-0.14} IO_3^- \xrightarrow{-0.7} H_3IO_6^{2-}$$

with -0.49

The physical and chemical properties of the halogen oxides and the halogen oxyacids are discussed in Sec. 4.7-4.9. It will be noticed that all the chemical properties are predictable from, or at least consistent with,

Table 4.5   PROPERTIES OF SOME BINARY MOLECULAR HALIDES

	Melting Point (°C)	Boiling Point (°C)		Melting Point (°C)	Boiling Point (°C)
PCl_3	−92	74.2	$GeCl_4$	−49.5	83.1
PBr_3	−40.5	172.8	$GeBr_4$	26.1	187.1
PI_3	61.2	d. > 200	GeI_4	144.0	0.7 mm 110° (subl)
$AsCl_3$	−13	130	BCl_3	−107	12.4
$AsBr_3$	35	220	BBr_3	−46	90.5
AsI_3	146	403	BI_3	49	210
$SiCl_4$	−68	57.0	Al_2Cl_6	192	180.1(subl)
$SiBr_4$	5.2	152.8	Al_2Br_6	97.5	265
SiI_4	120.5	290	Al_2I_6	191	386

the oxidation potentials on page 36. In acidic solutions HOCl, $HClO_2$, ClO_3^-, HOBr, and HOI are thermodynamically unstable with respect to disproportionation, and the species Cl_2, ClO_4^-, BrO_3^-, and H_5IO_6 are thermodynamically unstable because they are capable of oxidizing water to oxygen (H_2O-O_2, −1.23 v). However, all these species decompose slowly enough to be observed in solution. (In fact, perchloric acid solutions are kinetically stable indefinitely under ordinary conditions.) In basic solutions, all the halogen species in the diagram on page 36 except the halide ions, the perchlorate ion, and the iodate ion, are thermodynamically unstable. However, of the unstable species, the only ones which decompose rapidly under ordinary conditions are the free halogens:

$$X_2 + 2\,OH^- \longrightarrow X^- + OX^- + H_2O$$

The equilibrium constants for a large number of reactions are calculable from the data on page 36. Consider the interactions of the halogen species among themselves in acid solutions. The various possible reactions may be indicated on a matrix such as that in Table 4.6, where the principal products of the reactions are given in the appropriate rectangles. Consider the reaction of iodide with bromate. From the magnitudes of the potentials, it is clear that bromate can oxidize iodide, but the products cannot be predicted without specifying the mole ratio of the reactants. When iodide is in excess it is impossible to oxidize the iodine beyond the zero oxidation state (actually I_3^- forms in the presence of the excess iodide) because any higher oxidation state (e.g., iodate) would be reduced by the excess iodide to the zero oxidation state. The bromate reduction does not stop at elementary bromine because the excess iodide reduces bromine to bromide. Thus we predict the reaction

$$9\,I^- + BrO_3^- + 6\,H^+ \longrightarrow 3\,I_3^- + Br^- + 3\,H_2O$$

When bromate is in excess, the bromine cannot be reduced beyond the elementary state because bromide is oxidized by bromate. The oxidation

Table 4.6   INTERACTIONS OF THE HALOGEN SPECIES IN ACID SOLUTION
(N.R. SIGNIFIES NO REACTION)

Species in Insufficiency

Species in Excess	Cl^-	Cl_2	ClO_3^-	Br^-	Br_2	BrO_3^-	I^-	I_2	IO_3^-	H_5IO_6
Cl^-	—	—	Cl_2	—	N.R.	$Br_2 + Cl_2$	—	N.R.	N.R.	$IO_3^- + Cl_2$
Cl_2	—	—	N.R.	$Br_2 + Cl^-$	N.R.	$Br_2 + ClO_3^-$	$IO_3^- + Cl^-$	$IO_3^- + Cl^-$	N.R.	$IO_3^- + ClO_3^-$
ClO_3^-	Cl_2	N.R.	—	$Br_2 + Cl_2$	N.R.	N.R.	$IO_3^- + Cl_2$	$IO_3^- + Cl_2$	N.R.	N.R.
Br^-	—	$Cl^- + Br_2$	$Cl^- + Br_2$	—	—	Br_2	—	N.R.	$I_2 + Br_2$	$I_2 + Br_2$
Br_2	N.R.	N.R.	N.R.	—	—	N.R.	$I_2 + Br^-$	N.R.	N.R.	$IO_3^- + BrO_3^-$
BrO_3^-	$ClO_3^- + Br_2$	$ClO_3^- + Br_2$	N.R.	Br_2	N.R.	—	$IO_3^- + Br_2$	$IO_3^- + Br_2$	N.R.	—
I^-	—	$Cl^- + I_3^-$	$Cl^- + I_3^-$	—	$Br^- + I_3^-$	$Br^- + I_3^-$	—	I_3^-	I_3^-	I_3^-
I_2	N.R.	$Cl^- + IO_3^-$	$Cl^- + IO_3^-$	N.R.	N.R.	$Br_2 + IO_3^-$	I_3^-	—	N.R.	IO_3^-
IO_3^-	N.R.	N.R.	N.R.	$Br_2 + I_2$	N.R.	N.R.	I_2	N.R.	—	—
H_5IO_6	$ClO_3^- + IO_3^-$	$ClO_3^- + IO_3^-$	N.R.	$BrO_3^- + IO_3^-$	$BrO_3^- + IO_3^-$	—	IO_3^-	IO_3^-	—	—

of iodide does not stop at elementary iodine because iodine is oxidizable to iodate by the excess bromate. Thus we predict the reaction

$$5\,I^- + 6\,BrO_3^- + 6\,H^+ \longrightarrow 5\,IO_3^- + 3\,Br_2 + 3\,H_2O$$

In order to simplify the data of Table 4.6, it was assumed that chlorate cannot be oxidized to perchlorate, that none of the interhalogens is stable, and that the only polyhalide of importance is triiodide.

4.7 CHLORINE OXIDES AND OXYACIDS.   **Chlorine(I) oxide,** Cl_2O, is an explosive compound which melts at $-116°$ and boils at $2.0°$. It is the anhydride of **hypochlorous acid,** HOCl:

$$Cl_2O(g) + H_2O(l) = 2\,HOCl(aq) \qquad K = 280$$

The oxide is made by passing chlorine over mercuric oxide:

$$2\,Cl_2 + 2\,HgO \longrightarrow HgO \cdot HgCl_2 + Cl_2O$$

The molecule is V-shaped, with a ClOCl bond angle of $111°$.

Chlorine undergoes a small but measurable amount of hydrolysis (disproportionation) in aqueous solution:

$$Cl_2 + H_2O = H^+ + Cl^- + HOCl \qquad K = 4.66 \times 10^{-4}$$

The formation of hypochlorous acid can be carried to completion by the addition of a species which can react with the hydrogen ion or chloride ion, or both. One such species is mercuric oxide, which reacts to form

$HgO \cdot HgCl_2$. Another such species is bicarbonate, which is too weak a base to react with the HOCl:

$$Cl_2 + HCO_3^- \longrightarrow HOCl + CO_2 + Cl^-$$

Of course, strong base carries the disproportionation to completion with formation of **hypochlorite.**

The ionization constant of hypochlorous acid is 3.2×10^{-8}. Solutions of hypochlorite are sold as bleaching agents under various trade names. The bleaching action is attributable to the strong oxidizing action of hypochlorite. Hypochlorite solutions liberate oxygen in the presence of catalysts such as cobalt hydroxide. When heated, the solutions decompose to chloride and chlorate:

$$3 OCl^- \longrightarrow 2 Cl^- + ClO_3^-$$

The rate of this disproportionation has been observed to be second order in hypochlorite, suggesting the mechanism

$$2 OCl^- \xrightarrow{\text{slow}} ClO_2^- + Cl^-$$

$$ClO_2^- + OCl^- \xrightarrow{\text{fast}} ClO_3^- + Cl^-$$

The reaction proceeds more rapidly in solutions of lower pH, where the rate-determining steps

$$HOCl + OCl^- \longrightarrow H^+ + Cl^- + ClO_2^-$$
and
$$2 HOCl \longrightarrow 2 H^+ + Cl^- + ClO_2^-$$

become important. These latter reactions might be expected to be faster because they do not involve the collision of two similarly charged ions.

Chlorine dioxide, ClO_2, is the most thoroughly studied of the oxides of chlorine—this attention probably being due to the industrial use of the gas as a bleaching agent. The compound melts at $-59°$ and boils at $11.0°$; it is yellow in the gaseous state, red-brown as a liquid, and red-yellow as a solid. Chlorine dioxide may be prepared by the action of sulfuric acid on potassium chlorate in the presence of a reducing agent. Oxalic acid serves well because the ClO_2 is then diluted with CO_2 and manipulation is relatively free from danger of explosions:

$$2 HClO_3 + H_2C_2O_4 \longrightarrow 2 ClO_2 + 2 H_2O + 2 CO_2$$

The molecule is V-shaped, with an OClO bond angle of $117.4°$. The compound is paramagnetic because it has an odd number of electrons. In aqueous alkali, chlorine dioxide reacts to give both **chlorite** and **chlorate;**

hence it may be looked upon as the mixed anhydride of chlorous and chloric acids:

$$2\,ClO_2 + 2\,OH^- \longrightarrow ClO_2^- + ClO_3^-$$

It is tempting to look upon this reaction as the result of an electron exchange between two ClO_2 molecules:

$$2\,ClO_2 \longrightarrow ClO_2^- + ClO_2^+$$

$$ClO_2^+ + 2\,OH^- \longrightarrow ClO_3^- + H_2O$$

Chlorous acid is formed in aqueous solution by the reaction between chlorine dioxide and hydrogen peroxide:

$$2\,ClO_2 + H_2O_2 \longrightarrow 2\,HClO_2 + O_2$$

The acid, for which an ionization constant of 1.1×10^{-2} has been reported, decomposes to chlorine and chlorine dioxide. Alkaline solutions are much more stable, but decompose on boiling:

$$3\,ClO_2^- \longrightarrow 2\,ClO_3^- + Cl^-$$

Chlorate is formed by the disproportionation of hypochlorite (see above). The preparation may be effected by passing chlorine into a hot alkaline solution or by electrolyzing a hot chloride solution. The latter process is carried out in weakly acid solutions (*ca.* pH 6.8) in order to favor the disproportionation. Dichromate is added to inhibit the cathodic reduction of the chlorate. Solutions of chloric acid may be obtained by the precipitation of an insoluble salt of the cation; thus sulfuric acid will yield chloric acid from barium chlorate, and fluorosilicic acid will yield the acid from the potassium salt. The acid is completely ionized in aqueous solution. Chloric acid has not been obtained in the pure state, but concentrated aqueous solutions are moderately stable when kept cool and in the dark. The acid slowly disproportionates into chloride and perchlorate and oxidizes water to oxygen.

Potassium chlorate is the most important salt of chloric acid. It is well known to freshman chemistry students because of its use in the preparation of oxygen. When potassium chlorate is heated to 400–500°, the following reactions take place:

$$2\,KClO_3 \longrightarrow 2\,KCl + 3\,O_2$$

$$4\,KClO_3 \longrightarrow 3\,KClO_4 + KCl$$

$$KClO_4 \longrightarrow KCl + 2\,O_2$$

These reactions are susceptible to catalysis by potassium chloride and transition metal oxides. By the addition of MnO_2, the first of these reactions is caused to proceed at a convenient rate at 150°. However, then the evolved oxygen is contaminated with as much as 3 percent chlorine dioxide.

Dichlorine hexoxide, Cl_2O_6, has been prepared by (1) the reaction of chlorine with ozone, (2) the photochemical decomposition of chlorine dioxide, and (3) the reaction of chlorine dioxide with ozone. The latter reaction is most commonly used for the laboratory preparation. The oxide melts at 3.5° and has an extrapolated boiling point of 203°. In the vapor state it exists principally as the paramagnetic molecule ClO_3; in the liquid state the molecules are largely dimerized to Cl_2O_6. In many of its reactions, dichlorine hexoxide behaves as if it were chloryl perchlorate, $ClO_2^+ClO_4^-$. Thus hydrogen fluoride reacts as follows:

$$Cl_2O_6 + HF = HClO_4 + ClO_2F$$

As indicated above, **potassium perchlorate** can be prepared by the controlled thermal decomposition of potassium chlorate. This salt is soluble to the extent of only 0.75 grams in 100 ml of water at 0°, whereas most other metal perchlorates are quite soluble. Thus, soluble perchlorates are sometimes used for the qualitative analysis of potassium ion, and vice versa. Perchlorates can also be prepared by the anodic oxidation of chlorates. The latter oxidation is much more difficult to achieve than might be suggested by the ClO_3^-—ClO_4^- oxidation potential (-1.19 v in acid solutions). Only extremely powerful oxidizing agents such as peroxydisulfate and sodium bismuthate are capable of effecting the oxidation.

Perchloric acid is obtained by the vacuum distillation of a mixture of sulfuric acid and a perchlorate solution. A constant boiling mixture containing 72.4 percent $HClO_4$, having a composition approximating that of the dihydrate, is the usual laboratory reagent. By vacuum distillation of the 72 percent acid with fuming sulfuric acid, 75 percent yields of the anhydrous perchloric acid (mp $-112°$) can be obtained. This is a very reactive chemical; it explosively oxidizes organic materials such as wood, paper, rubber, etc. The extreme reactivity of anhydrous perchloric acid may be due to the presence of equilibrium concentrations of **perchloric anhydride,** Cl_2O_7:

$$2\,HClO_4 = H_2O + Cl_2O_7$$

The latter compound is a very explosive liquid with a freezing point of $-95.5°$ and a boiling point of 80°. It is prepared by the dehydration of perchloric acid with phosphorus(V) oxide:

$$2\,HClO_4 + P_2O_5 \longrightarrow 2/x\,(HPO_3)_x + Cl_2O_7$$

When perchloric acid is diluted to a concentration of 72 percent, it is much less reactive and generally has little oxidizing power except at elevated temperatures. Mixtures with many reducing agents are nevertheless hazardous. In dilute solutions, the **perchlorate ion** is essentially inert toward most reducing agents, even in boiling solutions. The ion has practically no basic character and forms very weak complexes with only a few highly charged metal ions. The nonreactivity of the perchlorate ion makes it a favorite inert anion in physical chemical studies. It is interesting that the isoelectronic species, ClO_4^-, and **perchloryl fluoride,** $FClO_3$, have similar reactivities. The latter compound is extraordinarily stable. Hydrolysis to fluoride and perchlorate takes place only in concentrated alkali at 200–300°. Iodide is oxidized only in strongly acidic solutions:

$$FClO_3 + 8\,I^- + 7\,H^+ \longrightarrow 4\,I_2 + HF + Cl^- + 3\,H_2O$$

Perchloryl fluoride can be made by (1) the action of fluorine on potassium chlorate at −40°

$$KClO_3 + F_2 \longrightarrow KF + FClO_3$$

(2) the reaction of sodium perchlorate with excess fluorosulfonic acid at 60–70°

$$NaClO_4 + 2\,HSO_3F \longrightarrow FClO_3 + H_2S_2O_7 + NaF$$

and (3) the reaction of perchloric anhydride, Cl_2O_7, with fluorine at 100°

$$Cl_2O_7 + F_2 \longrightarrow FClO_3 + ClO_2F + O_2$$

Chloryl fluoride, ClO_2F, may be prepared by the reaction of chlorine dioxide with various powerful fluorinating agents such as fluorine and AgF_2. The compound is fairly stable toward thermal decomposition; it melts at −115° and boils at −6°. As might be expected, chloryl fluoride hydrolyzes in aqueous alkali to give chlorate and fluoride:

$$ClO_2F + 2\,OH^- \longrightarrow ClO_3^- + F^- + H_2O$$

4.8 BROMINE OXIDES AND OXYACIDS. **Bromine(I) oxide,** Br_2O, may be prepared analogously to Cl_2O by the reaction of bromine with mercuric oxide:

$$2\,Br_2 + 2\,HgO \longrightarrow HgO \cdot HgBr_2 + Br_2O$$

The dark brown solid oxide is stable only at low temperatures; it melts with partial decomposition at −17.5°. Br_2O dissolves in water to form **hypobromous acid,** but solutions of the latter substance are more conveniently prepared by the disproportionation of aqueous bromine. In the absence of species which can remove bromide from solution, the disproportionation proceeds to only a slight extent:

$$Br_2 + H_2O = HOBr + H^+ + Br^- \qquad K = 5.8 \times 10^{-9}$$

The reaction can be carried to completion by HgO or silver ion:

$$2\,Br_2 + 2\,HgO + H_2O \longrightarrow 2\,HOBr + HgO \cdot HgBr_2$$

$$Br_2 + Ag^+ + H_2O \longrightarrow HOBr + AgBr + H^+$$

Hypobromous acid has an ionization constant of 2.1×10^{-9} and decomposes readily to bromide and bromate. Hypobromite solutions may be prepared by adding bromine to cold aqueous alkali:

$$Br_2 + 2\,OH^- \longrightarrow OBr^- + Br^- + H_2O$$

When a cold mixture of ozone and oxygen is passed into a solution of bromine in a fluorochlorocarbon such as $CFCl_3$ at $-50°$, a quantitative yield of **bromine dioxide,** BrO_2 is obtained:

$$Br_2 + 4\,O_3 \longrightarrow 2\,BrO_2 + 4\,O_2$$

The unstable oxide may be isolated by distilling off the solvent. At low temperatures, bromine dioxide reacts with strong fluorinating agents such as bromine pentafluoride to give **bromyl fluoride:**

$$5\,BrO_2 + BrF_5 \longrightarrow \tfrac{1}{2}\,Br_2 + 5\,BrO_2F$$

The latter compound forms volatile, colorless crystals which melt at $-9°$. The liquid decomposes above room temperature.

Bromates are readily prepared by adding bromine to hot basic solutions:

$$3\,Br_2 + 6\,OH^- \longrightarrow BrO_3^- + 5\,Br^- + 3\,H_2O$$

If potassium hydroxide is used, potassium bromate can be fractionally crystallized out. Bromates are generally less soluble than chlorates, and may be distinguished by the insolubility of silver bromate. Although bromates are stable in alkaline solution, solutions of **bromic acid** decompose into bromine and oxygen.

$$4\,H^+ + 4\,BrO_3^- \longrightarrow 2\,H_2O + 2\,Br_2 + 5\,O_2$$

Bromous acid and **bromites** are unknown, as are **perbromic acid** and **perbromates.** The nonexistence of stable compounds of bromine in the $+7$ oxidation state is difficult to understand, because $+7$ compounds of both chlorine and iodine are known. However, perhaps one should be surprised at the existence of $+7$ iodine compounds, rather than at the nonexistence of $+7$ bromine compounds. It is interesting that this discontinuity in the $+7$ oxidation state of the halogens is paralleled by discontinuities in the $+6$ state of the oxygen family and in the $+5$ state of the nitrogen family. Thus neither $AsCl_5$ nor $AsBr_5$ is known, although the corresponding halides of phosphorus and antimony are known; and the oxyacids of As(V) and Se(VI) have greater oxidizing power than the oxyacids of Sb(V) and Te(VI), respectively.

4.9 IODINE OXIDES AND OXYACIDS. Although the corresponding oxide is unknown, **hypoiodous acid** may be prepared analogously to hypobromous and hypochlorous acids:

$$2\, HgO + 2\, I_2 + H_2O \longrightarrow HgI_2 \cdot HgO + 2\, HOI$$

The solution is very unstable, decomposing within a few minutes into iodide and iodate. **Hypoiodite** solutions may be prepared by dissolving iodine in cold alkaline solutions or by the oxidation of iodide by hypochlorite. The disproportionation to iodide and iodate is somewhat slower in alkaline solutions than in acid solutions. HOI is the weakest of the hypohalous acids; the ionization constant at 25° is about 10^{-11}. Relatively stable complexes of I^+ cations are formed in the reaction of hypoiodous acid with chloride to form ICl and ICl_2^-, and in the formation of various iodine(I) compounds such as $I(py)_2NO_3$ (py = pyridine). Thus silver nitrate reacts with an equimolar amount of iodine and an excess of pyridine in chloroform as follows:

$$AgNO_3 + I_2 + 2\, py \longrightarrow I(py)_2NO_3 + AgI$$

Electrolysis of $I(py)_2NO_3$ in chloroform yields I_2 at the cathode only—indicating the existence of $I(py)_2^+$ ions. Iodine dissolves in oleum (sulfuric acid containing dissolved SO_3) to form a blue, paramagnetic solution which is believed to contain I^+ cations having two unpaired electrons.

Iodic acid, HIO_3, is a white solid that is very soluble in water and only slightly soluble in concentrated nitric acid. The solid precipitates when iodine is oxidized by concentrated nitric acid. Solutions of the pure acid may be prepared by the reaction of stoichiometric amounts of chloric acid with iodine (the resulting chlorine being volatile) and by the reaction of hydrogen peroxide with iodine. The acid anhydride, **diiodine pentoxide,** may be prepared by dehydration of the acid at approximately 240°:

$$2\, HIO_3 \longrightarrow I_2O_5 + H_2O$$

The pentoxide is a white solid that decomposes at 300° to iodine and oxygen. A mixture of I_2O_5, SiO_2, and H_2SO_4 quantitatively oxidizes carbon monoxide to carbon dioxide even at room temperature.

Iodic acid dissolves sparingly in sulfuric acid; it is believed that **iodyl bisulfate,** IO_2HSO_4, forms:

$$HIO_3 + 2\, H_2SO_4 \longrightarrow IO_2HSO_4 + H_3O^+ + HSO_4^-$$

On long standing, a white precipitate forms which is probably a polymeric form of **$(IO_2)_2SO_4$.** When iodic acid is heated with sulfuric acid, oxygen is evolved, and a diamagnetic yellow solid—usually referred to as I_2O_4, or **iodosyl iodate**, $IOIO_3$—is formed:

$$2\,HIO_3 + H_2SO_4 \longrightarrow I_2O_4 + H_3O^+ + HSO_4^- + \tfrac{1}{2}O_2$$

I_2O_4 is decomposed by hot water:

$$5\,I_2O_4 + 4\,H_2O \longrightarrow I_2 + 8\,IO_3^- + 8\,H^+$$

The compound I_4O_9 is prepared by heating concentrated phosphoric acid with iodic acid or by the reaction of ozone with iodine; the structure may correspond to $I(IO_3)_3$.

Iodyl fluoride, IO_2F, may be prepared by the reaction of fluorine with I_2O_5 in anhydrous hydrogen fluoride:

$$I_2O_5 + F_2 \longrightarrow 2\,IO_2F + \tfrac{1}{2}O_2$$

The solution may be treated with BF_3 or AsF_5 to form $IO_2(BF_4)$ or $IO_2(AsF_6)$; it seems likely that the latter compounds contain the iodyl cation, IO_2^+. Alkali metal **difluoroiodates** such as KIO_2F_2 are prepared by evaporating solutions of the corresponding iodates in 40 percent hydrofluoric acid:

$$IO_3^- + 2\,HF \longrightarrow IO_2F_2^- + H_2O$$

The iodine atom of the $IO_2F_2^-$ ion is surrounded by four atoms and an unshared pair of valence electrons situated at the corners of a trigonal bipyramid. The structure is analogous to that of SF_4 (see Fig. 3.1 and Table 3.4), with the two fluorine atoms occupying apical positions and the two oxygen atoms occupying equatorial positions. The lone pair of electrons occupies an equatorial position because in this location it (1) occupies a hybrid atomic orbital (sp^2) having considerable s character and (2) suffers a minimum of repulsion by adjacent atoms (two F atoms each at 90°, as opposed to three atoms at 90° if it occupied an "apical" position).

Periodates are prepared by the oxidation of iodates by hypochlorite in concentrated sodium hydroxide solution; the sparingly soluble disodium paraperiodate precipitates:

$$2\,Na^+ + IO_3^- + OCl^- + OH^- + H_2O \longrightarrow Na_2H_3IO_6 + Cl^-$$

In aqueous solution, **periodic acid** exists as the para acid, H_5IO_6. The first two ionization constants are known:

$$H_5IO_6 = H^+ + H_4IO_6^- \qquad K_{25°} = 5.1 \times 10^{-4}$$
$$H_4IO_6^- = H^+ + H_3IO_6^{2-} \qquad K_{25°} = 2.0 \times 10^{-7}$$

However, a large fraction of the -1 ions are dehydrated and exist in the meta form, IO_4^-:

$$H_4IO_6^- = IO_4^- + 2\,H_2O \qquad K_{25^\circ} = 40$$

It is not very often that dehydration-hydration equilibria of this type can be studied in aqueous solution. In this case it is possible because the two species have different ultraviolet absorption spectra. Crystalline para-periodic acid is prepared by the low-temperature evaporation of its aqueous solutions; vacuum desiccation yields the meta acid, HIO_4. Slightly soluble **meta salts,** such as KIO_4, may be precipitated by the addition of the appropriate metal ions to solutions of periodic acid.

Periodyl fluoride may be prepared by a method analogous to that used for preparing iodyl fluoride; metaperiodic acid is fluorinated in anhydrous hydrogen fluoride:

$$HIO_4 + F_2 \longrightarrow IO_3F + HF + \tfrac{1}{2}O_2$$

Periodyl fluoride is a white solid which hydrolyzes slowly in aqueous alkali.

$$IO_3F + 3\,OH^- \longrightarrow H_3IO_6^{2-} + F^-$$

4.10 ANALYSIS. The precipitation of silver chloride ($K_{sp} = 2.8 \times 10^{-10}$), silver bromide ($K_{sp} = 5 \times 10^{-13}$) and silver iodide ($K_{sp} = 8.5 \times 10^{-17}$) is used for both the qualitative and quantitative analyses of these halides. The silver halides all dissolve in aqueous thiosulfate solutions,

$$AgX + 2\,S_2O_3^{2-} = Ag(S_2O_3)_2^{3-} + X^-$$

but only the chloride dissolves in aqueous ammonia:

$$AgCl + 2\,NH_3 = Ag(NH_3)_2^+ + Cl^-$$

The bromide and iodide ions may be distinguished, after oxidizing them to the elementary state with an oxidizing agent such as chlorine, by the colors of the elements when extracted into a solvent such as carbon tetrachloride.

In the Volhard method for the quantitative analysis of halides, the halide solution is treated with an excess of standard silver nitrate solution, and the excess silver nitrate is determined by titration with standard thiocyanate solution:

$$Ag^+ + SCN^- \longrightarrow AgSCN(s)$$

Ferric ion is used as an indicator in the titration; a trace of excess thiocyanate gives a red color because of the formation of complexes such as $FeSCN^{2+}$ and $Fe(SCN)_2^+$.

Elementary chlorine and bromine and all the halogen species of positive oxidation state (except perchlorate) can be quantitatively determined by their reduction by excess iodide, followed by titration of the triiodide with standardized thiosulfate solution:

$$2\,S_2O_3{}^{2-} + I_3{}^- \longrightarrow 3\,I^- + S_4O_6{}^{2-}$$

This latter titration is one of the most precise and important titrations in quantitative analysis. The titration is usually carried out in the presence of soluble starch, which is colored deep blue in the presence of triiodide, and the end point is recognized by the disappearance of color. Many oxidizing agents, such as Cu^{2+}, $MnO_4{}^-$, $Cr_2O_7{}^{2-}$, and Ce^{4+}, can be determined by reducing them with excess iodide and titration of the triiodide with thiosulfate. Many reducing agents, such as Sn^{2+}, $SO_3{}^{2-}$, and H_3AsO_3, can be determined by direct titration with standardized triiodide or by reaction with a known excess of triiodide followed by titration with thiosulfate.

Iodide may be determined by titration in 6 M HCl with a strong oxidizing agent such as iodate or permanganate. The titration is usually carried out under an atmosphere of CO_2 to avoid aerial oxidation of the iodide, while the solution is agitated with a small amount of chloroform or carbon tetrachloride. The first step of the reaction involves the conversion of the iodide to I_2Cl^-:

$$2\,I^- + Cl^- = I_2Cl^- + 2\,e^-$$

The second step involves the conversion of the I_2Cl^- to $ICl_2{}^-$:

$$I_2Cl^- + 3\,Cl^- = 2\,ICl_2{}^- + 2\,e^-$$

Throughout the titration, the chloroform or carbon tetrachloride is colored violet by the presence of free iodine. At the end point, this color disappears; only a very low concentration of weakly colored ICl is present in the solution.

Soluble perchlorates may be gravimetrically analyzed by precipitation of the sparingly soluble potassium perchlorate. Ignition of perchlorates with ammonium chloride in the presence of a little platinum catalyst results in reduction to the chlorides, which may be determined as silver chloride.

SUGGESTED REFERENCES

Brasted, R. C., "The Halogens," in Vol. III of *Comprehensive Inorganic Chemistry,* M. C. Sneed, J. L. Maynard, and R. C. Brasted, eds. New York: Van Nostrand, 1954.

Latimer, W. M., *Oxidation Potentials,* 2nd ed. Englewood Cliffs, N.J.: Prentice-Hall, 1952.

Mellor, J. W., *Mellor's Comprehensive Treatise on Inorganic and Theoretical Chemistry,* Supplement II, Part I. London: Longmans, Green and Co., 1956. A comprehensive discussion of the halogens.

Sanderson, R. T., *Chemical Periodicity.* New York: Reinhold, 1960. A correlative discussion of the halides.

Schmeisser, M., and K. Brändle, "Oxides and Oxyfluorides of the Halogens," *Advances in Inorg. Chem. and Radiochem.,* 5 (1963), 42.

5

Oxygen

5.1 OCCURRENCE AND PREPARATION.
About one-half by weight of the
earth's crust is composed of oxygen;
oxygen exists as the molecule O_2 in air
(20.91 volume percent), as water in the
oceans and ice packs, and principally
as oxides of silicon and aluminum in
the solid crust.

The fractional distillation of liquid
air is the main commercial source of
elementary oxygen. Nitrogen boils
at $-195.8°$, and oxygen boils at
$-183.0°$; consequently, with a good
fractionating column these two com-
ponents of air can be separated from
each other. Oxygen is formed in the
electrolysis of aqueous solutions, but
oxygen from this relatively expensive
process is only a by-product of hydrogen production. A variety of methods
has been used for the laboratory preparation of oxygen. In Sec. 4.7 we discussed the MnO_2-catalyzed decomposition of potassium chlorate. Other
oxygen-evolving thermal decomposi-
tions which may be included here are
the following:

$$KNO_3 \longrightarrow KNO_2 + \tfrac{1}{2}O_2$$

$$BaO_2 \longrightarrow BaO + \tfrac{1}{2}O_2$$

$$HgO \longrightarrow Hg + \tfrac{1}{2}O_2$$

$$2\,KMnO_4 \longrightarrow K_2MnO_4 + MnO_2 + O_2$$

The first three of these reactions are reversible. The last reaction is often used for the preparation of very pure oxygen.

5.2 PHYSICAL PROPERTIES. Some of the important physical properties of atomic and molecular oxygen are summarized in Table 5.1.

The oxygen molecule is highly paramagnetic, indicating the presence of unpaired electrons. This paramagnetism certainly would not have been predicted using the simple Lewis octet theory. The simplest electronic structure having an octet of valence electrons around each atom corresponds to a diamagnetic molecule, $\ddot{O}=\ddot{O}$. However, by using a set of five electrons of one spin, $\cdot O \vdots O \cdot$, and a set of seven electrons of the opposite spin, $\overset{x}{\underset{x}{\times}}O \times O \overset{x}{\underset{x}{\times}}$, we can achieve a structure having an octet of electrons around each atom and two $(7 - 5)$ unpaired electrons. The latter configuration corresponds to the ground-state molecule. It is more instructive, however, to consider the molecule from the point of view of molecular orbitals. The overlap of an atomic orbital on one atom with the corresponding atomic orbital on another atom leads to the formation of two molecular orbitals, one bonding and one antibonding. Consequently the $2s$ and three $2p$ orbitals of the oxygen atoms in O_2 give rise to eight molecular orbitals, as shown in Fig. 5.1. It is significant that two pairs of π-type molecular orbitals of identical energies are formed as a result of the overlap of the two pairs of p orbitals which are perpendicular to the molecular axis. The electronic configuration of O_2 is achieved by adding the 12 valence electrons to the molecular orbitals. When we have added 10 valence electrons, corresponding to $O_2{}^{2+}$, all the electrons are paired in the lowest available energy levels. The next two electrons, because they electrostatically repel each other, enter the $\pi_p{}^*$ orbitals separately, and thus the

Table 5.1 SOME PROPERTIES OF OXYGEN

Atomic Oxygen:

Ionization potential, kcal/mole	
one electron	315.45
two electrons	1127.46
Electron affinity, kcal/mole	
$O + e^- \rightarrow O^-$	*ca.* 30
$O + 2e^- \rightarrow O^{2-}$	*ca.* -170

Molecular Oxygen:

Melting point, °C	-218.8
Boiling point, °C	-183.0
Heat of vaporization, kcal/mole	1.63
Solubility in water at 1 atm, 25°, M	1.3×10^{-3}
Dissociation energy, kcal/mole	118.0
Critical temperature, °C	-118.4
Critical pressure, atm	50.14
Ionization potential, ev	12.08
O—O bond distance, Å	1.207

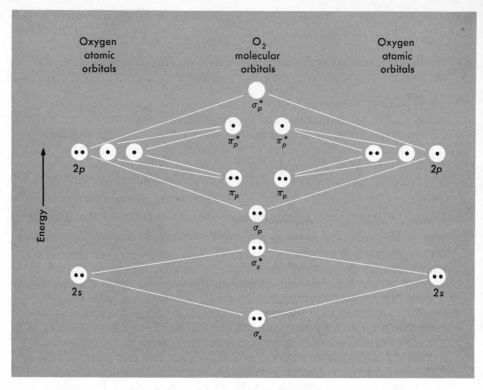

FIGURE 5.1 *The correlation of oxygen atomic orbitals with oxygen molecular orbitals.*

molecule is paramagnetic. Incidentally, since there are four more bonding electrons than antibonding electrons, the molecule is double-bonded.

Molecular oxygen absorbs light weakly in the red region of the spectrum, the transition corresponding to the pairing of the two unpaired electrons. This absorption is apparent in liquid oxygen, which is blue. The molar magnetic susceptibility of oxygen dissolved in liquid nitrogen decreases with increasing concentration of O_2. This behavior is explained by the formation of the very weakly-bound diamagnetic O_4 molecule:

$$2\,O_2 = O_4 \qquad \Delta H° = -0.13 \text{ kcal/mole}$$

5.3 CHEMICAL PROPERTIES OF OXYGEN. Oxygen forms thermodynamically stable oxides with all the elements except a few transition metals, nitrogen, the heavier halogens, and the noble gases. In some cases, the oxides form slowly from the elements at ordinary temperatures (e.g., the oxidation of the alkali and alkaline-earth metals and the rusting of iron), but high temperatures are generally required in order to effect reasonably rapid oxidation. Many metals, such as aluminum and cerium, react very slowly with gaseous oxygen because of protective oxide coatings which form on the metal surfaces. The oxidation potentials for oxygen are given in the diagrams shown on page 51. By reference to a table of oxidation potentials,

Acidic Solutions:

$$H_2O \xrightarrow{-1.77} H_2O_2 \xrightarrow{-0.67} O_2$$
$$\underset{-1.23}{\rule{6cm}{0.4pt}}$$

Basic Solutions:

$$OH^- \xrightarrow{-0.87} HO_2^- \xrightarrow{0.08} O_2$$
$$\underset{-0.40}{\rule{6cm}{0.4pt}}$$

it is apparent, from the magnitude of the H_2O-O_2 potential, that oxygen is capable of oxidizing a multitude of species in aqueous solution. Again, however, the reactions are generally slow at ordinary temperatures. The slowness of many oxidations by molecular oxygen in aqueous solutions is attributable to the fact that **hydrogen peroxide** is usually an intermediate in such reactions. When reducing agents with oxidation potentials between those of the peroxide-oxygen and water-oxygen couples are oxidized, the formation of peroxide is a slow step because of the energy barrier. Thus the oxidation potential of the bromide-bromine couple is -1.07 v, and although oxygen is capable of oxidizing bromide, the reaction is very slow. On the other hand, iodide (with an oxidation potential of -0.54 v) is a stronger reducing agent than peroxide, and it reacts with oxygen at a moderate rate in acid solutions:

$$6\,I^- + O_2 + 4\,H^+ \longrightarrow 2\,I_3^- + 2\,H_2O$$

The very strong reducing agents Cr^{2+}, Ti^{3+}, $Cu(NH_3)_2^+$, and V^{2+} rapidly reduce oxygen and are sometimes used to remove traces of oxygen from gases such as nitrogen and hydrogen.

One of the most important reactions of molecular oxygen is that with the protein hemoglobin. Each molecule of hemoglobin contains in its structure four ferrous ion complexes having basic structures like the one pictured in Fig. 5.2. Each of these units is believed to be attached to the protein by two links from the organic ring system around the iron atom, and by coordination of a nitrogen atom of the protein to the iron atom. In aqueous solutions, the sixth coordination position of the iron is probably occupied by a water molecule. However, this water molecule is displaced by an oxygen molecule upon exposure of the hemoglobin to a sufficiently

FIGURE 5.2 *The iron(II) complex in hemoglobin. Four nuclei of this type, with substituents on the periphery of the ring system, are found in hemoglobin.*

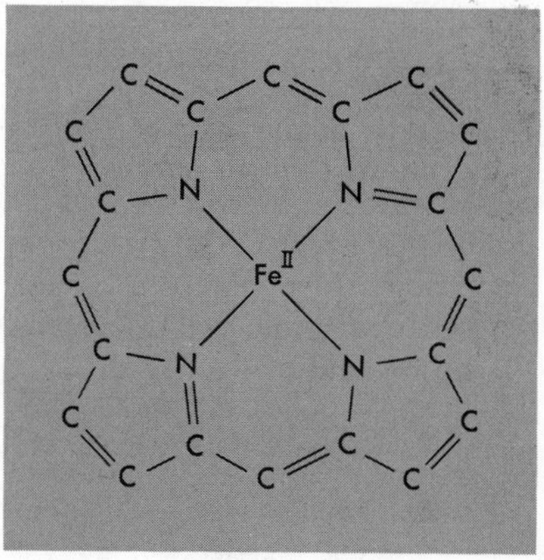

high partial pressure of oxygen. The reaction may be reversed by pumping off the oxygen. Thus hemoglobin is uniquely constructed for the purpose of oxygen transport in blood. Both carbon monoxide and the cyanide ion coordinate to the ferrous ions of hemoglobin more strongly than does oxygen. These reagents owe their extremely poisonous character to their ability to prevent the coordination of oxygen in complexes of this type.

5.4 OXIDES. The oxides of the nonmetals are discussed in the appropriate chapters of this book. Some of the oxides of the metals, most of which consist of ionic lattices containing the O^{2-} ion, are listed in Table 5.2 along with their heats of formation, their melting points, and their acid-base character in aqueous solutions. Note that the stability of the alkali metal oxides increases with decreasing molecular weight, just as in the case of the alkali metal hydrides and fluorides (see Sec. 1.8 and 3.4). The stability of the alkaline earth oxides reaches a maximum at calcium oxide. Note also that, within families of metal oxides, the trend in melting point is usually the same as the trend in stability. Inasmuch as the melting point would be expected to rise with increasing lattice energy, this is evidence for the dominant effect of the lattice energy in determining the thermodynamic stability of these compounds. The parenthesized notations in Table 5.2 give the acid-base character of the metal oxides in non-complexing aqueous solutions. Strong bases such as sodium oxide react with water to form completely ionized hydroxide solutions:

$$Na_2O + H_2O \longrightarrow 2\,Na^+ + 2\,OH^-$$

Weak bases such as magnesium oxide react with water to form the hydroxide which is only slightly soluble in water. In many cases the conversion to the hydroxide does not take place, but the basic character can be demonstrated by dissolving the oxide in acid. Amphoteric oxides such as aluminum oxide dissolve in acids to form the metal cations

$$Al_2O_3 + 6\,H^+ \longrightarrow 2\,Al^{3+} + 3\,H_2O$$

and dissolve in bases to form anions

$$Al_2O_3 + 2\,OH^- + 7\,H_2O \longrightarrow 2\,Al(H_2O)_2\,(OH)_4^-$$

Weakly acidic oxides such as antimony(V) oxide dissolve in alkaline solutions to form anions:

$$Sb_2O_5 + 2\,OH^- + 5\,H_2O \longrightarrow 2\,Sb(OH)_6^-$$

Strongly acidic oxides such as CrO_3 dissolve in water to give solutions of strong acids:

$$2\,CrO_3 + H_2O \longrightarrow 2\,H^+ + Cr_2O_7^{2-}$$

5.5 **WATER.** We have already discussed some of the distinctive charac-teristics of water in the chapter on hydrogen (hydrogen bond, Sec. 1.11; the aqueous proton, Sec. 1.12).

The structure of ordinary, low-density ice is shown in Fig. 1.3. More compact structures can be prepared by subjecting ice to high pressures.

Table 5.2   HEATS OF FORMATION, MELTING POINTS, AND ACID-BASE CHARACTER OF METAL OXIDES

Oxide*	$-\Delta H_f^\circ, 25^\circ$ kcal/mole	Melting Point, (°C)	Oxide*	$-\Delta H_f^\circ, 25^\circ$ kcal/mole	Melting Point, (°C)
Li_2O (s.b.)	142.4	1730	TcO_2 (i.)	103.4	
Na_2O (s.b.)	99.4	917	ReO_3 (a.)	147	160
K_2O (s.b.)	86.4	>490	Re_2O_7 (s.a.)	297	296
Rb_2O (s.b.)	79.0	477			
Cs_2O (s.b.)	76	490	$Fe_{0.95}O$ (w.b.)	63.8	1377
			Fe_3O_4 (i.)	267.8	1597
BeO (amph.)	143.1	2550	Fe_2O_3 (amph.)	196.8	
MgO (w.b.)	143.8	2800	RuO_2 (i.)	56.5	>955
CaO (s.b.)	150.6	2590	OsO_4 (w.a.)	94	56
SrO (s.b.)	141.1	2460			
BaO (s.b.)	133.5	1923	CoO (w.b.)	57.0	1805
RaO (s.b.)	130		Co_3O_4 (i.)	207	
			RhO (w.b.)	21.5	
Sc_2O_3 (w.b.)	411		Rh_2O_3 (w.b.)	68.5	
Y_2O_3 (w.b.)	420	2400	IrO_2 (w.b.)	40	>1100
La_2O_3 (w.b.)	428.5	2320			
Ce_2O_3 (w.b.)	435		NiO (w.b.)	57.3	1960
CeO_2 (w.b.)	245	2730	PdO (w.b.)	22.9	
Ac_2O_3 (w.b.)	444				
ThO_2 (w.b.)	293.2	2950	Cu_2O (w.b.)	40.4	1229
			CuO (amph.)	37.6	1447
UO_2 (w.b.)	259.2	2700	Ag_2O (amph.)	7.2	
U_3O_8 (w.b.)	853.5		Au_2O_3 (amph.)	0.8	
UO_3 (amph.)	291				
NpO_2 (w.b.)	246		ZnO (amph.)	83.2	1975
PuO_2 (w.b.)	246	>1900	CdO (amph.)	62.2	>1230
AmO_2 (w.b.)	240		HgO (amph.)	21.7	
TiO (w.b.)	123.9		Al_2O_3 (amph.)	399.6	2030
TiO_2 (amph.)	225.5	1855	Ga_2O_3 (amph.)	258	1725
ZrO_2 (amph.)	261.5	2690	In_2O_3 (amph.)	221.2	
HfO_2 (amph.)	266.0	2790	Tl_2O_3 (w.b.)	98	717
V_2O_5 (amph.)	373	670	SnO (amph.)	68.4	
Nb_2O_5 (amph.)	455.2	1512	SnO_2 (amph.)	138.8	1625
Ta_2O_5 (amph.)	488.8	1880	PbO (amph.)	52.4	886
			PbO_2 (amph.)	66.1	
Cr_2O_3 (amph.)	272.6	2440			
CrO_3 (s.a.)	140	198	Sb_2O_3 (amph.)	169.9	655
MoO_3 (w.a.)	180.3	795	Sb_2O_5 (w.a.)	229	
WO_3 (w.a.)	200.8	1470	BiO	50	
			Bi_2O_3 (w.b.)	138	817
MnO (w.b.)	92.0	1785			
MnO_2 (i.)	124.4				

* Acid-base character: s.b., strong base; amph., amphoteric; w.b., weak base; s.a., strong acid; w.a., weak acid; i., inert; a., acid.

The particular structure obtained is determined by the magnitudes of the temperature and pressure; a portion of the temperature-pressure phase diagram for water is shown in Fig. 5.3. Notice that, for pressures less than 2047 atm, the freezing point of water (that is, the temperature at which ice-I is in equilibrium with liquid water) decreases with increasing pressure. This is the effect expected for a substance whose molar volume is greater in the solid phase than in the liquid phase. However, the molar volumes of the high-pressure ice phases are lower than the molar volume of liquid water. Hence the normal increase in melting point with increasing pressure is observed for pressures greater than 2047 atm.

Liquid water is very unusual in having a temperature, 3.98°, of maximum density. (The density rises from 0.99987 at 0° to 1.00000 at 3.98°, and then gradually decreases to 0.9584 at 100°.) When ice melts at 0°, the low-density hydrogen-bonded structure is only partially broken down. As the temperature is raised, more hydrogen bonds are broken, and the water molecules arrange themselves in a manner more closely resembling the closest packing of spheres. Thus at first the density of water increases with increasing temperature. However, at 3.98°, the breakdown in structure does not increase rapidly enough with temperature to compensate for the normal positive temperature coefficient of volume caused by the increase in thermal energy of the molecules. Consequently, at higher temperatures, the density decreases with increasing temperature. An appreciable amount of hydrogen-bonding remains in liquid water even at 100°, as evidenced by the high entropy of vaporization, $\Delta S° = 26.0$ cal deg^{-1} mole^{-1}. (Normal, unassociated liquids have entropies of vaporization in the neighborhood of 21 cal deg^{-1} mole^{-1}.)

In the gaseous state, the water molecule is V-shaped, with an H—O—H bond angle of 104.5° and an O—H bond distance of 0.96 Å. The molecule has a dipole moment of 1.85 Debyes. This rather high dipole moment is largely responsible for the fact that water is an excellent solvent for many

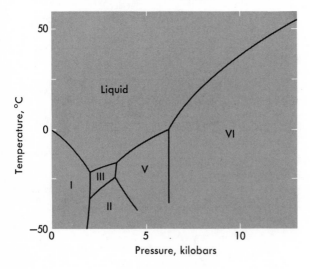

FIGURE 5.3 *Phase diagram for water and the ices. 1 kilobar = 987 atmospheres.*

ionic compounds and compounds which can dissociate into ions. Large amounts of energy are required to break up such compounds into their constituent ions, and this energy often can be got back in the interaction of the dipolar water molecules with the charged ions. It is believed that water molecules coordinate themselves to cations with the oxygen atoms pointing in, and to anions with the hydrogen atoms pointing in.

The structure of the water molecule may be explained in various ways; we shall here give two ways. (1) An oxygen atom in its ground state has an electronic configuration $1s^2 2s^2 2p^4$. Two of the $2p$ electrons are paired; two of them are unpaired and occupy separate $2p$ orbitals whose axes are mutually perpendicular. The $2s$ and $2p$ orbitals which are occupied by the four paired electrons may be considered to be hybridized as two equivalent orbitals pointing directly opposite to each other. Thus these orbitals with the higher electron density are as far apart as possible. If we were to form the water molecule by bringing up two hydrogen atoms along the axes of the p orbitals containing the unpaired electrons, we might expect the H—O—H bond angle in water to be 90°. (See Fig. 5.4.) However, when we form two O—H bonds by thus using pure p orbitals of the oxygen atom, we increase the electron density in the regions between the oxygen atom and the hydrogen atoms. Because these bonding electron pairs are in orbitals which make a 90° angle, they are fairly close to each other and electrostatically repel each other. This repulsion is minimized by a widening of the bond angle with an attendant rehybridization of the orbitals. Some s character is diverted to the bonding orbitals, and some p character to the non-bonding orbitals. The rehybridization does not proceed so far as to make all four orbitals equivalent (sp^3 hybridization). As the H—O—H angle increases, the angle between the very highly repulsive lone-pairs of electrons decreases; a balance is achieved when the H—O—H angle is less than the tetrahedral angle (109°28') and when the angle between the lone-pair orbitals is greater than this angle. (See Fig. 5.5.) (2) From the foregoing discussion, one might mistakenly suppose that a consideration of the directional characteristics of p orbitals was essential to understanding the nonlinear structure of the water molecule. However, as we shall now show, the nonlinear structure would have been anticipated purely from a consideration of the polarizability of the oxide ion. Let us imagine forming a water molecule by the reaction of two protons with an oxide ion. If the oxide ion were a hard, nondistortable sphere, the most stable configuration would be that in which both

FIGURE 5.4 *Schematic, hypothetical representation of the formation of a water molecule by the overlap of the 1s orbitals of two hydrogen atoms with two 2p orbitals of an oxygen atom. The two lone pairs of electrons in the oxygen atom's valence shell are imagined to occupy two sp hybrid orbitals perpendicular to the plane of the molecule.*

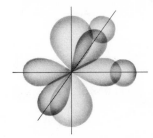

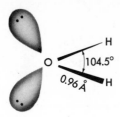

O ∠104.5°
0.96 Å
H

protons lie on the surface of the sphere, making an H—O—H angle of 180°. Of course, the oxide ion does not behave as a hard, nondistortable sphere. When a proton approaches an oxide ion, the electron cloud is distorted so as to increase the electron density in the direction of the proton and to decrease the electron density on the opposite side of the oxide ion. Thus the oxide ion is polarized and achieves an induced electric moment. The proton is therefore held to the oxide ion more strongly than if the oxide ion were nondistortable. When a second proton approaches the ion, it does not come in at an angle of 180°, because then the induced moments would be opposed and there would be no binding energy due to polarization. However, when the second proton forms its bond at an angle of less than 180°, the oxide ion is polarized along a line which bisects the H—O—H bond angle, and the system is stabilized by the interaction between the resultant induced dipole and the protons. As the H—O—H angle decreases, the polarization stabilization increases and the proton-proton electrostatic repulsion increases. The observed bond angle corresponds to a balance of these effects. (See Fig. 5.6.)

Miscellaneous physical properties of water are presented in Table 5.3.

5.6 OZONE.

Ozone, O_3, is a pungent gas often smelled in the vicinity of discharging high-voltage apparatus and sometimes noticed during thunderstorms. It occasionally reaches concentrations as high as one part per million in smog, and can be detected by the cracking of stretched rubber bands. Ozone is an unstable allotrope of oxygen:

$$\tfrac{3}{2}O_2 \longrightarrow O_3 \qquad \Delta F_{25^\circ} = 39.1\ \text{kcal/mole}$$

It may be prepared in three different ways. The simplest and most efficient method is the electric discharge method, in which oxygen, at atmospheric pressure, is passed through the annular space between two concentric glass tubes across which a potential of 10,000–20,000 volts is applied. (See Fig. 5.7.) Concentrations as high as 5 percent are easily obtained. A second method for preparing ozone is the irradiation of oxygen with ultraviolet light. This method is used for the prep-

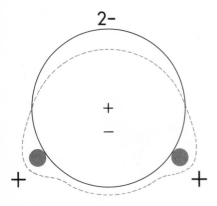

2−
+
−
+   +

Table 5.3   SOME PHYSICAL PROPERTIES OF WATER

Melting point in air	273.150° K or 0° C
Triple point	273.160° K or 0.010° C
Boiling point	100° C
Critical temperature	374.0° C
Critical pressure	217.7 atm
Heat of formation, ΔH_f°, at 25°	−68.317 kcal/mole
Heat of vaporization at bp	9.717 kcal/mole
Heat of fusion at 0°	1.436 kcal/mole
Heat capacity at 25°	17.996 cal/deg mole
Dielectric constant at 25°	78.54
Surface tension against air at 25°	71.97 dynes/cm
Viscosity at 25°	0.8937 centipoise
Conductivity at 18°	4×10^{-8} mho/cm
Ionization constant at 25°	1.002×10^{-14}
Heat of ionization at 25°	13.36 kcal/mole

aration of low concentrations of ozone for sterilization and disinfection purposes. A large amount of ozone is produced photochemically in the stratosphere. In a third preparative method, the electrolytic one, cold aqueous solutions of sulfuric or perchloric acid are electrolyzed with extremely high anodic current densities. Oxygen and, in the case of sulfuric acid solutions, peroxydisulfuric acid, $H_2S_2O_8$, are by-products.

Ozone condenses to a blue, explosive liquid which melts at −192.5° and boils at −111.9°. The molecule is V-shaped, with a bond angle of 116.8°. The O—O bond distance, 1.28 Å, is between that expected for a single bond (1.48 Å in H_2O_2) and that for a double bond (1.21 Å in O_2). The structure may be explained by the resonance

$$\overset{\cdot\cdot}{\underset{-O}{O}}\diagup\overset{O^+}{\diagdown}O \longleftrightarrow O\diagup\overset{\overset{\cdot\cdot}{O^+}}{\diagdown}O^-$$

Ozone is a powerful oxidizing agent. In most of its reactions, only one

FIGURE 5.7   *Silent electric discharge apparatus for the preparation of ozone.*

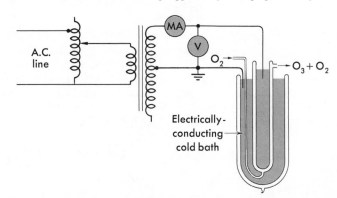

of the oxygen atoms is transferred, and O_2 is formed as a product. The following reactions are examples of this behavior:

$$2\,NO_2 + O_3 \longrightarrow N_2O_5 + O_2$$

$$3\,I^- + O_3 + 2\,H^+ \longrightarrow I_3^- + O_2 + H_2O$$

$$2\,H^+ + 2\,Co^{2+} + O_3 \longrightarrow 2\,Co^{3+} + O_2 + H_2O$$

The oxidation-reduction couples for ozone and the corresponding potentials are as follows:

$$O_2 + H_2O = O_3 + 2\,H^+ + 2\,e^- \qquad E^\circ = -2.07$$

$$O_2 + 2\,OH^- = O_3 + H_2O + 2\,e^- \qquad E^\circ = -1.24$$

5.7 PEROXIDES, SUPEROXIDES AND OZONIDES. Hydrogen peroxide, H_2O_2, is prepared by the hydrolysis of peroxo-compounds—that is, compounds containing the —O—O— linkage. Thus the **peroxydisulfate ion** (formed by the anodic oxidation of sulfuric acid or sulfate) undergoes stepwise hydrolysis in acid solution:

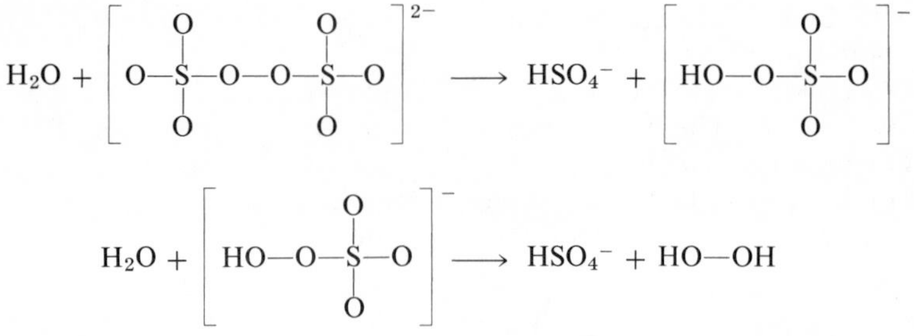

Since the first of these steps is faster than the second, the **peroxymonosulfate** intermediate **(Caro's acid)** may be isolated. The latter species reacts with hydrogen peroxide to form oxygen:

$$HSO_5^- + H_2O_2 \longrightarrow HSO_4^- + H_2O + O_2$$

To avoid this reaction in the preparation of hydrogen peroxide, the hydrolysis is carried out under reduced pressure, and the H_2O_2 distils to form an approximately 30 weight percent solution. We have already pointed out that many oxidations by molecular oxygen involve the formation of hydrogen peroxide as the reduction product of the oxygen. A commercially important example of this type of reaction is the oxidation of isopropanol to acetone and hydrogen peroxide:

$$(CH_3)_2CHOH + O_2 \longrightarrow (CH_3)_2CO + H_2O_2$$

The oxidation of compounds such as 2-ethyl-anthrahydroquinole is also used for the preparation of hydrogen peroxide:

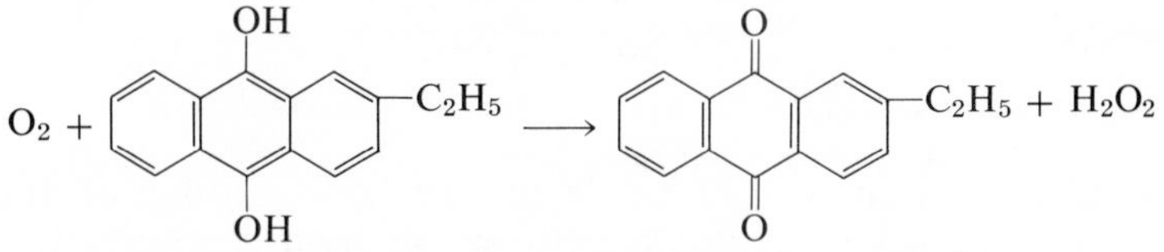

$$O_2 + \text{(structure)} \longrightarrow \text{(structure)} \; C_2H_5 + H_2O_2$$

The anthraquinone is catalytically hydrogenated back to the starting material, which can be used again.

Pure hydrogen peroxide may be obtained by the fractional distillation of aqueous hydrogen peroxide under reduced pressure. The pure compound is very much like water in many of its physical properties. It melts at $-0.4°$, boils at $150.2°$ (extrapolated), and has a dielectric constant at $20°$ of 73.1. The material is very unstable toward decomposition to water and oxygen, particularly at high temperatures, and so it is usually used in aqueous solutions. However, some applications, such as its use as an oxidant in rocket propulsion, require the pure, or highly concentrated, compound. In aqueous solutions, hydrogen peroxide is a very weak acid: $K_1 = 2.4 \times 10^{-12}$. The second ionization constant is much smaller, so ionic peroxides dissolve in water with complete hydrolysis to the HO_2^- ion:

$$Na_2O_2 + H_2O \longrightarrow 2\,Na^+ + HO_2^- + OH^-$$

From the oxidation potential diagram on page 51 we see that hydrogen peroxide is a powerful oxidizing agent. However, it is ordinarily a fairly slow oxidizing agent. Thus the oxidation of iodide

$$3\,I^- + H_2O_2 + 2\,H^+ \longrightarrow I_3^- + 2\,H_2O$$

proceeds measurably slowly even though it has a large driving force. In acid solution, the rate law is

$$\text{Rate} = k(H_2O_2)(H^+)(I^-)$$

and the following mechanism has been proposed to explain the rate law:

$$H_2O_2 + H^+ \underset{\text{fast}}{\overset{\text{fast}}{\rightleftharpoons}} H_2O{-}OH^+$$

$$H_2O{-}OH^+ + I^- \xrightarrow{\text{slow}} HOI + H_2O$$

$$HOI + 2\,I^- + H^+ \xrightarrow{\text{fast}} I_3^- + H_2O$$

The slow step may be looked upon as the displacement of water from the hydroxyoxonium ion by the iodide ion. From the oxidation potential diagram we also see that hydrogen peroxide is a fairly strong reducing agent. Again, however, the reactions are usually slow, except with powerful oxidizing agents. Peroxide may be quantitatively oxidized by permanganate:

$$5 H_2O_2 + 2 MnO_4^- + 6 H^+ \longrightarrow 2 Mn^{2+} + 5 O_2 + 8 H_2O$$

The reaction of chlorine with an alkaline peroxide solution or of hypochlorite with an acidic hydrogen peroxide solution gives rise to a red chemiluminescence. The reactions may be written:

$$Cl_2 + HO_2^- + OH^- \longrightarrow 2 Cl^- + H_2O + O_2{}^*$$

$$O_2{}^* \longrightarrow O_2 + h\nu$$

Spectra of the chemiluminescence show that the excited oxygen is produced in a singlet state (no unpaired electrons) as opposed to the stable triplet state (two unpaired electrons) of normal oxygen.

One of the most interesting reactions of hydrogen peroxide is its self-oxidation-reduction:

$$2 H_2O_2 \longrightarrow 2 H_2O + O_2$$

In the absence of catalysts, this reaction is negligibly slow. However, a wide variety of substances, including platinum black, manganese dioxide, bromide or bromine, and ferrous or ferric ion, catalyze the reaction. Most of the homogeneous catalysts (the catalysts which are soluble in the peroxide solution) are oxidation-reduction couples of which the oxidizing agents are capable of oxidizing hydrogen peroxide and of which the reducing agents are capable of reducing hydrogen peroxide. From the oxidation potential diagram on page 51 we see that, in acid solutions, any couple with an oxidation potential between -0.67 and -1.77 volts satisfies these requirements. The potentials for the $Br^- - Br_2$ and $Fe^{2+} - Fe^{3+}$ couples (-1.07 and -0.77 v, respectively) fall in this range. Thus for the bromine-catalyzed reaction we write:

$$2 Br^- + H_2O_2 + 2 H^+ \longrightarrow Br_2 + 2 H_2O$$

$$Br_2 + H_2O_2 \longrightarrow 2 Br^- + O_2 + 2 H^+$$

Net reaction: $\qquad 2 H_2O_2 \longrightarrow 2 H_2O + O_2$

and for the iron-catalyzed reaction we write:

$$2 Fe^{2+} + H_2O_2 + 2 H^+ \longrightarrow 2 Fe^{3+} + 2 H_2O$$

$$2 Fe^{3+} + H_2O_2 \longrightarrow 2 Fe^{2+} + O_2 + 2 H^+$$

Net reaction: $\qquad 2 H_2O_2 \longrightarrow 2 H_2O + O_2$

Many elements form peroxy-compounds—that is, compounds containing the —O—O— linkage. We have already discussed two examples: peroxodisulfuric acid and Caro's acid. Other examples are CrO_5, $H_2Mo_2O_{11}$, HOONO, $(HO)_2PO(OOH)$, and $Ti(OH)_3OOH$. These compounds may be made by the addition of H_2O_2 to solutions of the appropriate oxyacids or salts.

Peroxides are salts of hydrogen peroxide; they contain the O_2^{2-} anion. The alkali and alkaline-earth metals and zinc and cadmium form peroxides. **Sodium peroxide,** Na_2O_2, is prepared by heating sodium in oxygen; the salt finds much use as a vigorous oxidizing agent. **Barium peroxide,** BaO_2, is readily prepared by heating BaO in air or oxygen. This reversible reaction was once used as a method for isolating oxygen.

The alkali metals heavier than lithium form yellow **superoxides** containing the paramagnetic O_2^- anion. **Sodium superoxide,** NaO_2, is formed by heating sodium peroxide with high pressures of oxygen; the other alkali metal superoxides form at atmospheric pressure. Superoxides react with carbon dioxide as follows:

$$2\,MO_2 + CO_2 \longrightarrow M_2CO_3 + \tfrac{3}{2}O_2$$

and with cold water as follows:

$$2\,MO_2 + H_2O \longrightarrow 2\,M^+ + 2\,HO_2^- + O_2$$

Ozone reacts with the alkali metal hydroxides, except lithium hydroxide, to form **ozonides.** In the case of potassium hydroxide the reaction appears to be

$$3\,KOH + 2\,O_3 \longrightarrow 2\,KO_3 + KOH \cdot H_2O + \tfrac{1}{2}O_2$$

The pure ozonide may be extracted with liquid ammonia; it forms orange-red crystals. **Potassium ozonide** is reported to react with water as follows:

$$2\,KO_3 + H_2O \longrightarrow 2\,K^+ + 2\,OH^- + \tfrac{3}{2}O_2$$

5.8 ANALYSIS. The molecular oxygen content of a gaseous mixture may sometimes be determined by the difference in volume after removal of the oxygen by some reducing agent. Alkaline pyrogallol solutions, acidic chromous solutions, and hot (*ca.* 500°) copper are often used for this purpose.

Oxygen in the form of water vapor may be determined by weighing the water absorbed by a desiccant ($Mg(ClO_4)_2$, $CaSO_4$, P_4O_{10}, etc.) or by the gas-volumetric determination of the hydrogen formed in the reaction of the water with hot (700°) uranium. The water of crystallization of many salt hydrates may be determined from the change in weight on drying the salt. Traces of water in organic solvents may be determined by titration with the Karl Fischer reagent. This reagent consists of a solution of iodine, pyridine, and sulfur dioxide, in methanol. The reaction with water appears to proceed in two distinct steps:

$$3\,C_5H_5N + I_2 + SO_2 + H_2O \longrightarrow 2\,C_5H_5NH^+ + 2\,I^- + C_5H_5NSO_3$$

$$C_5H_5NSO_3 + CH_3OH \longrightarrow C_5H_5NH^+ + CH_3OSO_3^-$$

Freshly prepared reagent is deep reddish-brown, and the spent reagent is straw-yellow, hence the reagent may serve as its own indicator. However, the end point is usually determined electrometrically.

The oxygen content of a metal oxide is seldom directly determined because there is no simple general method for the analysis of oxygen in such a compound. The oxygen content of an oxide is often determined "by difference" after analyzing for all the other elements present. However, the oxygen may be determined gas-volumetrically after oxidizing it to molecular oxygen with bromine trifluoride. Thus oxides such as TiO_2 and Ta_2O_5 react with BrF_3 at $75°$ as follows:

$$3\,TiO_2 + 4\,BrF_3 \longrightarrow 3\,TiF_4 + 2\,Br_2 + 3\,O_2$$

$$6\,Ta_2O_5 + 20\,BrF_3 \longrightarrow 12\,TaF_5 + 10\,Br_2 + 15\,O_2$$

Extremely small amounts of oxygen (parts per million) in metals can be determined by bombardment of the metal with helium-3 nuclei from a cyclotron or linear accelerator. The oxygen nuclei are converted to fluorine-18 nuclei, which can be quantitatively determined by their positron emission: $_8O^{16}(He^3,p)_9F^{18}$, $_9F^{18} \longrightarrow _8O^{18} + \beta^+$.

Hydrogen peroxide may be detected by the formation of blue CrO_5 with an acidic solution of dichromate or by the formation of yellow $Ti(OH)_3OOH$ with titanium(IV) sulfate solution. Volumetric methods for the determination of peroxide have been based on the *reduction* of peroxide by mercury(I), arsenite, and iodide, and on the *oxidation* of peroxide by cerium(IV) and permanganate. The oxygen formed in the latter oxidation can be determined gas-volumetrically.

Superoxides can be analyzed by measurement of the oxygen evolved in their reaction with water. Ozonides may be analyzed by measurement of the oxygen evolved in their thermal decomposition:

$$KO_3 \longrightarrow KO_2 + \tfrac{1}{2}O_2$$

SUGGESTED REFERENCES

Brewer, L., "The Thermodynamic Properties of the Oxides and their Vaporization Processes," *Chem. Rev.,* 52 (1953), 1.

Coughlin, J. P., *Heats and Free Energies of Formation of Inorganic Oxides.* Washington: Bureau of Mines Bulletin 542, 1954.

Dorsey, N. E., *Properties of Ordinary Water-Substance.* New York: Reinhold, 1940.

Eichhorn, G. L., "Coordination Compounds in Natural Products," in J. C. Bailar, Jr., *The Chemistry of the Coordination Compounds.* New York: Reinhold, 1956, pp. 698–742. Contains a discussion of oxidation-reduction catalysts and oxygen-carrying complexes.

Latimer, W. M., *Oxidation Potentials,* 2nd ed. Englewood Cliffs, N.J.: Prentice-Hall, 1952.

Sanderson, R. T., *Chemical Periodicity.* New York: Reinhold, 1960. A correlative discussion of the oxides.

Schumb, W. C., *Hydrogen Peroxide.* New York: Reinhold, 1955.

6

Sulfur, Selenium,

and Tellurium

6.1 OCCURRENCE AND PREPARATION. **Sulfur,** constituting about 0.05 percent of the earth's crust, occurs mainly as the element (in large deposits in Louisiana and Texas), as sulfide minerals (such as iron pyrites, FeS_2), and as various sulfates (such as gypsum, $CaSO_4 \cdot 2\,H_2O$). The element is extracted in very pure form from the underground sulfur deposits in Louisiana and Texas by the Frasch process. Hot water is injected into cavities in the deposits, melting the sulfur and forcing it to the surface.

Selenium and **tellurium** are much less abundant than sulfur; they constitute about 10^{-5} percent and 10^{-7} percent, respectively, of the earth's crust, and frequently occur as trace constituents of metal sulfide ores. Selenium is obtained from the flue dusts produced in the roasting of sulfide ores, and as a by-product of sulfuric acid manufacture. Both selenium and tellurium are found in the anode sludge from the electrolytic refining of copper.

6.2 PHYSICAL AND CHEMICAL PROPERTIES OF THE ELEMENTS. Sulfur can exist in perhaps as many as 20 different solid modifications. **Orthorhombic sulfur,** also known as S_α, consists of 8-membered rings of sulfur atoms (S_8 molecules) and is the thermodynamically stable form up to 95.31°. Above 95.31° the stable form is **monoclinic**

sulfur, or S_β, which also consists of S_8 molecules, but in a different arrangement. The structure of the S_8 molecule is shown in Fig. 6.1. The $S_\alpha \leftrightarrow S_\beta$ conversion is slow; thus it is possible to keep S_β at room temperature for about a day, and one can rapidly heat S_α up to its melting point, 112.8°. The "ideal" melting point of S_β is 119.3°; that is, the temperature at which S_β is in equilibrium with a liquid consisting of S_8 rings. However, the S_8 rings in the liquid partly break down to chains (probably mainly S_8 chains), and this leads to a melting point depression which causes the "natural" melting point of S_β to be 114.6°. In practice, the melting point of sulfur is usually observed to lie between the values 114.6° and 119.3°.

A metastable, orange-yellow form of sulfur consisting of S_6 rings **(Engel's sulfur,** S_ϵ or S_ρ) may be prepared by adding concentrated hydrochloric acid to a concentrated solution of sodium thiosulfate at 0°, followed by extraction with toluene and crystallization by cooling.

When molten sulfur is heated above 159° and then is poured into cold water, a **plastic** form of sulfur, which consists of S_α and a CS_2-insoluble portion called S_μ, is formed. When plastic sulfur is stretched, strong fibers are formed which contain long helical chains of sulfur atoms.

All the known forms of sulfur are nonconductors of electricity. The S_α, S_β and S_ϵ forms are soluble in organic solvents; all forms are insoluble in water. Sulfur boils at 444.60°.

The stable form of **selenium** is the grey semimetallic form, which consists of infinite helical chains of selenium atoms. By evaporation of carbon disulfide solutions, two red modifications can be obtained, both of which consist of cyclic Se_8 molecules. Only one crystalline form of **tellurium** is known: the silvery, semimetallic form which is isostructural with grey selenium. The melting points of selenium and tellurium are 217° and 450°, respectively; the boiling points are 685° and 990°, respectively.

Much of the aqueous chemistry of sulfur, selenium, and tellurium is summarized in the oxidation potential diagrams on page 66. Notice that, in alkaline solutions, sulfur is unstable with respect to disproportionation into sulfide and thiosulfate. All the hydrides are readily oxidized to the corresponding elements by iodine and ferric ion. More powerful oxidizing agents, such as chlorine, will take the elements up to the $+6$ state.

6.3 HYDRIDES AND THEIR SALTS. One of the properties of most metals is that they react directly with sulfur, selenium, and tellurium to form the corresponding **sulfides, selenides,** and **tellurides.** In the case of the alkali and alkaline-earth metals, the compounds are principally ionic, containing S^{2-}, Se^{2-}, and Te^{2-} ions. Other metals form compounds having considerable covalent character and, in the case of some transition metals, metal-metal bonding and variable composition ranges. Thus six different **chromium**

FIGURE 6.1 *The "crown" configuration of the 8-membered ring of sulfur atoms in orthorhombic and monoclinic sulfur. All the atoms in the crown are equivalent.*

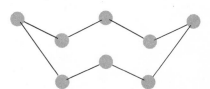

Acidic Solutions:

$$\text{H}_2\text{S} \xrightarrow{-0.14} \text{S} \xrightarrow{-0.50} \text{S}_2\text{O}_3{}^{2-} \xrightarrow{-0.08} \text{S}_4\text{O}_6{}^{2-} \xrightarrow{-0.51} \text{SO}_2(aq) \xrightarrow{-0.57} \text{S}_2\text{O}_6{}^{2-} \xrightarrow{0.22} \text{SO}_4{}^{2-}$$

with branches:

$$\text{S}_2\text{O}_3{}^{2-} \xleftarrow{\; -0.88 \;} \text{HS}_2\text{O}_4{}^- \xrightarrow{\; 0.08 \;}$$

$$-0.40 \; (\text{S}_2\text{O}_3{}^{2-} \to \text{SO}_2(aq)); \qquad -0.17 \; (\text{SO}_2(aq) \to \text{SO}_4{}^{2-})$$

$$-0.45 \; (\text{S} \to \text{SO}_2(aq))$$

$$\text{H}_2\text{Se} \xrightarrow{0.32} \text{Se} \xrightarrow{-0.74} \text{H}_2\text{SeO}_3 \xrightarrow{-1.15} \text{SeO}_4{}^{2-}$$

$$\text{H}_2\text{Te} \xrightarrow{0.44} \text{Te} \xrightarrow{-0.53} \text{TeO}_2(s) \xrightarrow{-1.02} \text{H}_6\text{TeO}_6(s)$$

Basic Solutions:

$$\text{S}^{2-} \xrightarrow{0.48} \text{S} \xrightarrow{0.74} \text{S}_2\text{O}_3{}^{2-} \xrightarrow{-0.08} \text{S}_4\text{O}_6{}^{2-} \xrightarrow{0.80} \text{SO}_3{}^{2-} \xrightarrow{0.93} \text{SO}_4{}^{2-}$$

with branches:

$$\text{S}_2\text{O}_3{}^{2-} \xleftarrow{\; 0.04 \;} \text{S}_2\text{O}_4{}^{2-} \xrightarrow{\; 1.12 \;}$$

$$0.58 \; (\text{S}_2\text{O}_3{}^{2-} \to \text{SO}_3{}^{2-}); \qquad 0.66 \; (\text{S} \to \text{SO}_3{}^{2-})$$

$$\text{Se}^{2-} \xrightarrow{0.84} \text{Se} \xrightarrow{0.37} \text{SeO}_3{}^{2-} \xrightarrow{-0.05} \text{SeO}_4{}^{2-}$$

$$\text{Te}^{2-} \xrightarrow{0.86} \text{Te} \xrightarrow{0.57} \text{TeO}_3{}^{2-} \xrightarrow{-0.4} \text{TeO}_2(\text{OH})_4{}^{2-}$$

sulfides, each with a small range of composition, are known: $\text{Cr}_{1.03}\text{S}$, $\text{Cr}_{0.88}\text{S}$—$\text{Cr}_{0.87}\text{S}$, $\text{Cr}_{0.85}\text{S}$, $\text{Cr}_{0.79}\text{S}$—$\text{Cr}_{0.76}\text{S}$, $\text{Cr}_{0.69}\text{S}$, $\text{Cr}_{0.67}\text{S}$. An usually wide range of composition is found in **cobalt telluride.** Here the composition ranges from CoTe to CoTe₂.

The alkali and alkaline-earth metal sulfides, selenides, and tellurides are soluble in water, but the anions are extensively hydrolyzed. For example:

$$\text{S}^{2-} + \text{H}_2\text{O} = \text{HS}^- + \text{OH}^- \qquad K \approx 1$$

Acidification of such solutions yields the corresponding gaseous hydrides, **H₂S, H₂Se,** and **H₂Te.** Some physical and chemical properties of these

Table 6.1 SOME PROPERTIES OF H_2S, H_2Se, AND H_2Te

	H₂S	H₂Se	H₂Te
Melting point, °C	−85.53	−65.73	−51
Boiling point, °C	−60.34	−41.3	−2.3
ΔH_f° at 25°, kcal/mole	−4.82	18.2	23.8
K_1 for $\text{H}_2\text{X} = \text{H}^+ + \text{HX}^-$	1.1×10^{-7}	1.9×10^{-4}	2.3×10^{-3}
K_2 for $\text{HX}^- = \text{H}^+ + \text{X}^{2-}$	10^{-14}	10^{-14}	10^{-11}
Solubility in H_2O at 25° and 1 atm, M	0.102	0.084	—

malodorous and poisonous hydrides are given in Table 6.1. Hot sulfide solutions dissolve sulfur to form chain **polysulfide ions** of general formula S_x^{2-}. Upon acidification, these solutions yield the **sulfanes,** H_2S_x. The lower members of this series, ranging from H_2S_2 to H_2S_6, have been isolated; they are yellow, oily liquids which readily decompose to hydrogen sulfide (H_2S) and sulfur.

6.4 OXIDES AND OXY-ACIDS. Sulfur dioxide, SO_2, (mp $-72.7°$, bp $-10.2°$) is formed by the oxidation of sulfur or sulfides. The molecule is a resonance hybrid of the structures $O{=}\!\!=\!\!S^{\pm}{-}O^-$ and $^-O{-}\!\!S^{\pm}\!\!=\!\!\!=O$; the bond angle is $119.5°$. Sulfur dioxide reacts sometimes as a Lewis base (with BF_3 it forms $F_3B{-}SO_2$) and sometimes as a Lewis acid (with the hydroxide ion it forms the bisulfite ion, $HOSO_2^-$). Aqueous solutions of sulfur dioxide (solubility at 1 atm and $25°$, $1.34\ M$) are often assumed to contain **sulfurous acid,** H_2SO_3; however there does not seem to be strong evidence for such a species. The equilibria in "sulfurous acid" solutions are probably best written:

$$SO_2(aq) + H_2O = H^+ + HSO_3^- \qquad K_{25°} = 1.3 \times 10^{-2}$$

$$HSO_3^- = H^+ + SO_3^{2-} \qquad K_{25°} = 6.2 \times 10^{-8}$$

In most of its applications, aqueous SO_2 functions as a reducing agent; sulfate is usually the oxidation product. The oxidation of SO_2 by excess iodate is a fascinating "clock" reaction. During the initial stage, the net reaction is

$$3\,SO_2 + IO_3^- + 3\,H_2O \longrightarrow 3\,HSO_4^- + I^- + 3\,H^+$$

Now, iodate oxidizes iodide to iodine fairly rapidly, but iodine oxidizes SO_2 even more rapidly. Consequently, the color of iodine is not observed until all of the SO_2 has been oxidized; when that point is reached, the solution suddenly turns brown (or blue, in the presence of starch).

Hot sulfite solutions dissolve sulfur with formation of **thiosulfate:**

$$S + SO_3^{2-} = S_2O_3^{2-}$$

Because sulfite is a stronger base than thiosulfate, the equilibrium is shifted to the left in acid solutions; a milky precipitate of sulfur is formed by the acidification of a thiosulfate solution.

The thiosulfate ion might conceivably have either a structure with equivalent sulfur atoms, such as $^-O{-}S{-}O{-}S{-}O^-$, or a structure with nonequivalent sulfur atoms, such as $^-S{-}\overset{\displaystyle O^-}{\underset{\displaystyle O^-}{\overset{|}{\underset{|}{S^{2+}}}}}O^-$. Only the second type of structure is compatible with the observation that, when thiosulfate is prepared from sulfite and radioactive sulfur and then decomposed to sulfide and sulfate (by decomposition of the silver salt), the radioactivity appears only in the sulfide:

$$S^* + SO_3{}^{2-} \longrightarrow S^*SO_3{}^{2-} \xrightarrow{Ag^+} Ag_2S^*SO_3 \xrightarrow[H_2O]{\Delta} Ag_2S^* + 2\,H^+ + SO_4{}^{2-}$$

Oxidation of thiosulfate by iodine (Sec. 4.10) yields the **tetrathionate ion,** ^-O_3S—S—S—$SO_3{}^-$. Strong oxidizing agents oxidize thiosulfate partly to sulfate and partly to **dithionate,** ^-O_3S—$SO_3{}^-$. Dithionate is relatively inert toward oxidizing agents, the reaction rate generally being controlled by the rate of hydrolysis to sulfate and bisulfite, the latter being rapidly oxidized.

Dithionite, $S_2O_4{}^{2-}$, may be prepared by the reduction of bisulfite, either cathodically or by metallic zinc. Although the ion is a very strong reducing agent in alkaline solution, it slowly disproportionates to thiosulfate and sulfite. Dithionite has the structure ^-O_2S—$SO_2{}^-$, with a remarkably long (2.39 Å) S—S bond.

Sulfur trioxide, SO_3, is formed by the reaction of SO_2 with O_2 (generally catalyzed by platinum, V_2O_5, or nitric oxide). Several crystalline forms of sulfur trioxide are known, the most important being the volatile γ—SO_3 (mp 16.8°) and the asbestos-like β—SO_3. The γ—SO_3 consists of S_3O_9

$$\begin{array}{c} O \\ \| \\ \text{—S—O—} \\ \| \\ O \end{array}$$

molecules, in each of which three —S—O— groups are linked together to form a 6-membered ring of alternating sulfur and oxygen atoms. The β—SO_3 consists of long chains of such SO_3 groups linked together.

Sulfur trioxide reacts with water to form **sulfuric acid,** H_2SO_4. In dilute aqueous solutions, the first ionization of sulfuric acid is complete, but the bisulfate ion, $HSO_4{}^-$, is a moderately weak acid: $K_{25°} = 1.26 \times 10^{-2}$. In such solutions, sulfuric acid reacts exceedingly slowly as an oxidizing agent. The concentrated acid is a somewhat more reactive oxidizing agent, and it is particularly effective as a dehydrating agent. In 100 percent sulfuric acid (mp 10.37°, bp 330°), although only a small fraction of the acid is ionized, the activity, or effective concentration, of the solvated hydrogen ion is enormous. Thus many species, such as water and phosphoric acid, are protonated when dissolved in sulfuric acid, and are therefore bases in this solvent:

$$H_2O + H_2SO_4 = H_3O^+ + HSO_4{}^-$$

$$H_3PO_4 + H_2SO_4 = P(OH)_4{}^+ + HSO_4{}^-$$

Sulfur trioxide dissolves in sulfuric acid to form **"fuming sulfuric acid"** or **"oleum,"** in which polysulfuric acids such as $H_2S_2O_7$ and $H_2S_3O_{10}$ exist. These are stronger acids than H_2SO_4.

Peroxydisulfuric acid and Caro's acid are discussed in Sec. 5.7.

SeO_2 (subl pt $\sim$320°, mp 340°) dissolves in water to form the moderately strong oxidizing agent, **selenous acid,** H_2SeO_3 ($K_1 = 2.7 \times 10^{-3}$, $K_2 = 2.5 \times 10^{-7}$). **TeO$_2$** is essentially insoluble in water, but dissolves in base to give **tellurite.** **SeO$_3$** has never been prepared pure, but **selenic acid,** H_2SeO_4 ($K_1 > 1$, $K_2 = 8.9 \times 10^{-3}$), is formed by the oxidation of selenous acid, and its properties are similar to those of sulfuric acid. **Telluric acid,** H_6TeO_6, is a weak dibasic acid ($K_1 \approx 10^{-7}$) which may be dehydrated to **TeO$_3$.**

6.5 HALIDES AND OXY-HALIDES. The physical properties of the fluorides of sulfur, selenium, and tellurium are given in Table 3.3. The properties of the other halides and the oxy-halides are given in Table 6.2.

Disulfur dichloride, S_2Cl_2, has a structure (Cl—S—S—Cl) analogous to that of hydrogen peroxide. It reacts slowly with water to form sulfur, sulfur

Table 6.2 SOME PROPERTIES OF THE HALIDES (EXCEPT FLUORIDES) AND OXY-HALIDES OF SULFUR, SELENIUM, AND TELLURIUM

Name	M. P. (° C)	B. P. (° C)
S_2Cl_2 Disulfur dichloride	−80	138
SCl_2 Sulfur dichloride	−78	d. 59
SCl_4 Sulfur tetrachloride	d. −31	
S_2Br_2 Disulfur dibromide	−46	d. 90
SOF_2 ⎫	−110	−43.8
$SOFCl$ ⎪ Thionyl halides	−139.5	12.2
$SOCl_2$ ⎬	−104.5	78.8
$SOBr_2$ ⎭	−49.5	d. 59
SOF_4 "Thionyl tetrafluoride"	−99.6	−49
SO_2F_2 ⎫	−136.7	−55.4
SO_2FCl ⎪ Sulfuryl halides	−124.7	7.1
SO_2FBr ⎬	−86.5	40
SO_2Cl_2 ⎭	−54.1	69.1
Se_2Cl_2 Diselenium dichloride	−85	d.
$SeCl_2$ Selenium dichloride	(known only in vapor state)	
$SeCl_4$ Selenium tetrachloride		subl 191
Se_2Br_2 Diselenium dibromide		d.
$SeBr_2$ Selenium dibromide	(known only in vapor state)	
$SeBr_4$ Selenium tetrabromide	d. 75	
$SeOF_2$ ⎫	15	126
$SeOCl_2$ ⎬ Selenyl halides	10.9	177
$SeOBr_2$ ⎭	41.7	
SeO_2F_2 Selenium dioxodifluoride	−99.5	−8.4
$TeCl_2$ Tellurium dichloride	208	328
$TeCl_4$ Tellurium tetrachloride	225	390
$TeBr_2$ Tellurium dibromide	210	339
$TeBr_4$ Tellurium tetrabromide	~380	~420
TeI_4 Tellurium tetraiodide	259	

dioxide, hydrochloric acid, and various oxy-acids such as pentathionic acid, $H_2S_5O_6$. The chlorination of S_2Cl_2 yields the unstable **sulfur dichloride,** SCl_2, which, at room temperature, is in equilibrium with appreciable amounts of chlorine and S_2Cl_2. The even more unstable **tetrachloride,** SCl_4, decomposes at its melting point to a mixture of SCl_2 and Cl_2. SF_6 is the principal product of the fluorination of sulfur. It is remarkable for its chemical inertness, being unaffected by molten KOH and steam at 500°. The preparation and fluorinating properties of SF_4 are discussed in Sec. 3.5.

The **halosulfuric acids,** $HOSO_2F$ (mp $-87°$, bp 162.6°), $HOSO_2Cl$ (mp $-80°$, bp 152°), and $HOSO_2Br$ (mp, dec, 8°), are prepared by the reaction of SO_3 with the appropriate hydrogen halides. Fluorosulfuric acid is hydrolyzed by water slowly, and chlorosulfuric acid explosively. Chlorosulfuric acid is often used in organic syntheses as a sulfonating agent—that is, a reagent for attaching the SO_3H group to molecules:

$$HOSO_2Cl + C_6H_6 \longrightarrow C_6H_5SO_2OH + HCl$$

6.6 SULFUR-NITROGEN COMPOUNDS. **Sulfur nitride,** S_4N_4, is generally prepared by the reaction of S_2Cl_2 or SCl_2 with ammonia in an inert solvent like carbon tetrachloride:

$$6\,S_2Cl_2 + 16\,NH_3 \longrightarrow S_4N_4 + 8\,S + 12\,NH_4Cl$$

$$6\,SCl_2 + 16\,NH_3 \longrightarrow S_4N_4 + 2\,S + 12\,NH_4Cl$$

S_4N_4 is a bright orange solid (mp 187°), insoluble in water but soluble in many organic solvents. The molecule is a puckered 8-membered ring (see Fig. 6.2), and is a resonance hybrid of structures such as:

$$
\begin{array}{ccc}
N\!-\!S\!=\!N \\
\| \qquad | \\
S \qquad\quad S \\
| \qquad\quad | \\
N\!-\!S\!-\!N
\end{array}
$$

S_4N_4 is the starting material for the synthesis of a large number of sulfur-nitrogen compounds. For example, S_2Cl_2 reacts with S_4N_4 to form **S_4N_3Cl:**

FIGURE 6.2 *The structure of the S_4N_4 molecule.*

$$3\,S_4N_4 + 2\,S_2Cl_2 \longrightarrow 4\,S_4N_3Cl$$

The latter compound is a salt containing the 7-membered planar ring:

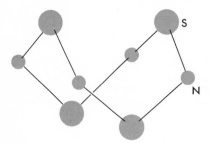

The $S_4N_3^+$ ion is kinetically stable in concentrated aqueous acids (e.g., 10 M H_2SO_4); in less acidic solutions it undergoes hydrolysis with eventual formation of sulfur, SO_2, and NH_4^+.

Amidosulfuric acid (sulfamic acid), $O_3S—NH_3$, may be prepared by the reaction of SO_3 with ammonia or by the reaction of urea with fuming sulfuric acid:

$$SO_3 + NH_3 \longrightarrow O_3SNH_3$$

$$H_2SO_4 + SO_3 + CO(NH_2)_2 \longrightarrow CO_2 + 2\,O_3SNH_3$$

In aqueous solution, the acid is quite strong ($K = 10^{-1}$), and, because the compound can be obtained in a state of high purity, it is used as a primary standard in acidimetry.

6.7 ANALYSIS. Acid-soluble **sulfides** are detected by treatment with acids; the liberated hydrogen sulfide may be identified by its odor, or by the PbS precipitate formed on filter paper moistened with lead acetate solution or sodium plumbite solution. Aqueous **hydrogen sulfide** may be analyzed quantitatively by its oxidation to sulfur with an excess of standard triiodide, followed by titration of the excess triiodide with standard thiosulfate. Elementary **sulfur** may be recognized by dissolving it in hot alkali and placing a drop of the solution on a silver coin, a black stain of Ag_2S indicating the presence of sulfur. **Sulfur dioxide** (such as that liberated by the acidification of a sulfite or thiosulfate) may be identified by passing it through a dilute solution containing permanganate and barium ions; simultaneous bleaching of the permanganate color and precipitation of barium sulfate constitutes a positive test. Aqueous sulfur dioxide may be quantitatively determined by oxidation to sulfate by excess standard triiodide followed by titration of the excess triiodide with standard thiosulfate. The precipitation of sulfate as barium sulfate ($K_{sp} = 1.5 \times 10^{-9}$) is used for both the qualitative and gravimetric analysis of **sulfate.**

Selenous and **selenic acids** are reduced to red selenium by sulfur dioxide in concentrated hydrochloric acid. Solutions of **TeO$_2$** and **telluric acid** in hot hydrochloric acid are reduced to elementary tellurium by the hydrazinium ion. These reactions may be used for the qualitative or gravimetric analysis of the elements. The +4 states of selenium and tellurium may be determined volumetrically by oxidation to the +6 states by permanganate.

SUGGESTED REFERENCES

George, J. W., "Halides and Oxyhalides of the Elements of Groups Vb and VIb," *Progress in Inorg. Chem.,* 2 (1960), 33.

Gillespie, R. J. and E. A. Robinson, "The Sulfuric Acid Solvent System," *Advances in Inorg. Chem. and Radiochem.,* 1 (1959), 385.

Meyer, B., "Solid Allotropes of Sulfur," *Chem. Rev.,* 64 (1964), 429.

Tobolsky, A. V., "Polymeric Sulfur and Other Polysulfide Polymers," *American Scientist,* 52 (1964), 358.

7

Nitrogen

7.1 ELEMENTARY NITROGEN. Nitrogen occurs principally as the relatively inert diatomic gas, N_2, which constitutes 78.09 percent by volume of dry air. Practically all nitrogen of commerce is produced by the liquefaction and fractional distillation of air. In the laboratory, nitrogen may be prepared by a variety of methods, most of which involve the oxidation of either ammonium ion or ammonia. Thus nitrogen is formed by the pyrolysis of ammonium nitrite and by the passage of ammonia over hot copper oxide. The thermal decomposition of sodium azide, NaN_3, to its elements is a source of spectroscopically pure nitrogen.

Nitrogen melts at $-209.97°$ and boils at $-195.79°$. The critical constants are $-146.89°$, 33.54 atm, and 90.1 cc/mole. The atoms are held together in the molecule by a triple bond: $:N \equiv N:$. The dissociation energy, 225.1 kcal/mole, is one of the highest known and accounts for the fact that, at ordinary temperatures, nitrogen is almost as inert as a noble gas.

When an electric discharge is established in nitrogen gas at low pressures, a peach-colored glow is emitted. When the discharge is turned off, the gas continues to give off a yellow "afterglow" for several minutes. The principal constituent of the activated gas, in addition to ordinary molecular nitrogen, is **atomic nitrogen.** The afterglow is caused by excited states of molecular nitrogen which form by the recombination of the N atoms. The concentration of atomic nitrogen in a stream of gas may be determined by "titrating" with nitric oxide:

$$N + NO \longrightarrow N_2 + O$$

If nitric oxide is added at a rate such that it is in excess, the unconsumed nitric oxide combines with the oxygen atoms formed, yielding a whitish- or greenish-yellow afterglow:

$$NO + O \longrightarrow NO_2 + h\nu$$

If nitric oxide is added so slowly that atomic nitrogen is in excess, the nitrogen atoms react with the oxygen atoms, giving a blue color:

$$N + O + M \longrightarrow NO + M + h\nu$$

When the quantities of nitric oxide and atomic nitrogen are equal, the gas is practically colorless.

7.2 AMMONIA, AMIDES, AND NITRIDES. **Ammonia** is manufactured by the Haber process, in which hydrogen and nitrogen react in the presence of an iron catalyst at pressures around 1000 atm and temperatures around 500°:

$$N_2(g) + 3 H_2(g) = 2 NH_3(g)$$

Ammonia melts at $-77.7°$ and boils at $-33.38°$. The molecule has the form of a pyramid with the nitrogen atom at the apex and the hydrogen atoms at the corners of the base, which is an equilateral triangle. (N—H distance, 1.014 Å; H—N—H angle, 106°47'.) Because of the N—H bond dipoles and the lone pair of electrons, ammonia has a rather large dipole moment, 1.47 Debye.

Liquid ammonia is a fairly good solvent for both inorganic and organic compounds, and it is often used as a reaction medium in synthetic chemistry. Ammonia is very slightly self-ionized:

$$2 NH_3 = NH_4^+ + NH_2^- \qquad K_{-33°} \approx 10^{-30}$$

This reaction may be compared with the self-ionization of water. The **ammonium ion,** NH_4^+, is analogous to the oxonium ion, H_3O^+, and the **amide ion,** NH_2^-, is analogous to the hydroxide ion, OH^-. Thus, neutralization reactions may be carried out by mixing solutions of ammonium salts (e.g., NH_4Cl) and amides (e.g., KNH_2). The very low ionization constant of ammonia may be taken advantage of when it is desired to work with strongly basic species which would be completely solvolyzed in more acidic solvents such as water. Thus, ions such as AsH_2^-, GeH_3^-, $C_6H_5NH^-$, and CH_3O^- are only slightly ammonolyzed in liquid ammonia.

Liquid ammonia possesses the remarkable property of being able to dissolve reversibly the highly electropositive metals (the alkali metals, the alkaline-earth metals except beryllium, and europium and ytterbium). The dilute solutions have a beautiful blue color (due to the short-wavelength tail of an absorption band at 15,000 Å), and the concentrated solutions have the appearance of molten bronze. In very dilute metal-ammonia solutions, the metal ions and metal valence electrons exist as independent ammoniated species, M^+_{am} and e^-_{am}. In solutions of moderate concentration $(0.01 - 1.0\ M)$, ionic aggregates of the following types are formed: $(M^+_{am})(e^-_{am})$, $(M^+_{am})(e^-_{am})_2$, and $(M^+_{am})_2(e^-_{am})_2$. Concentrated solutions $(\sim 10 M)$ are probably structurally analogous to molten metals; the valence electrons serve to bind together the ammoniated metal ions. Metal-ammonia solutions are metastable with respect to decomposition to hydrogen and the **metal amides:**

$$M^+_{am} + e^-_{am} + xNH_3 \longrightarrow x/2\,H_2 + M(NH_2)_x$$

This reaction is very slow if the solutions are kept cold and clean, but it can be made to proceed very rapidly by the addition of catalysts such as transition-metal salts.

Generally, when a metal amide is heated, deammoniation to the corresponding metal **nitride** occurs:

$$3\,Mg(NH_2)_2 \longrightarrow Mg_3N_2 + 4\,NH_3$$

A more convenient method for preparing nitrides is that in which the metal (or a mixture of the metal oxide and carbon) is heated with nitrogen or ammonia. This method is applicable to the following nitrides, all of which are thermodynamically stable with respect to the elements: Li_3N, Be_3N_2, Mg_3N_2, Ca_3N_2, Sr_3N_2, Ba_3N_2, Si_3N_4, Th_3N_4, *BN, AlN, ScN, YN, LaN, CeN, GaN, InN,* **TiN, ZrN, HfN, VN, NbN, TaN, Mo$_2$N, W$_2$N, UN, U$_2$N$_3$, Mn$_5$N$_2$, Mn$_3$N$_2$.** The nitrides whose formulas are given in regular type are examples of ionic nitrides; they contain N^{3-} ions in their crystal lattices. The nitrides with formulas in *italics* are *covalent* nitrides. (One example, boron nitride, is discussed in Sec. 11.8.) The nitrides with formulas in **boldface** type are **interstitial** or **metallic** nitrides. The latter usually have high melting points, extreme hardness, metallic conductivity, and relatively high chemical inertness.

Ammonia and water are miscible in all proportions. The **aqueous ammonia** of commerce contains about 28 percent by weight of NH_3 $(14.8\ M)$ and is in equilibrium with an ammonia partial pressure of 447 mm of Hg. A small fraction of the ammonia in aqueous solutions reacts as follows:

$$NH_3 + H_2O = NH_4^+ + OH^- \qquad K_{25^\circ} = 1.77 \times 10^{-5}$$

Thus solutions of most **ammonium salts** are weakly acidic because of the ionization of the ammonium ion:

$$NH_4^+ = H^+ + NH_3 \qquad K_{25°} = 5.65 \times 10^{-10}$$

At elevated temperatures most solid ammonium salts dissociate reversibly to gaseous ammonia and the corresponding protonic acids. For example:

$$NH_4HS(s) = NH_3(g) + H_2S(g)$$

When ammonium salts with oxidizing anions are heated, an irreversible reaction occurs in which an oxidation product of ammonia (e.g., N_2, N_2O, etc.) is formed:

$$NH_4NO_3 \longrightarrow N_2O + 2\,H_2O$$

Solutions of ammonium (NH_4) in mercury, called **ammonium amalgams,** may be prepared by the electrolysis of cold ammonium salt solutions, using a mercury cathode, or by the treatment of ammonium salt solutions with an alkali-metal amalgam. Ammonium amalgams are unstable at room temperature, decomposing to ammonia and hydrogen:

$$NH_4(Hg)_x \longrightarrow NH_3 + \tfrac{1}{2}H_2 + xHg$$

While decomposing, the amalgam is a voluminous, spongy mass because of the bubbles of gas being evolved.

7.3 NITROGEN-HALOGEN COMPOUNDS. The physical properties of the nitrogen fluorides are summarized in Table 3.3. The most important nitrogen fluoride is **NF_3**, an odorless, colorless gas which is prepared by the electrolysis of molten ammonium bifluoride or of solutions of ammonium bifluoride in anhydrous hydrogen fluoride. NF_3 is a remarkably unreactive material; it seems to have no basic properties whatsoever.

Aqueous solutions of **chloramine,** NH_2Cl, are prepared by the reaction of aqueous ammonia and hypochlorite:

$$NH_3 + OCl^- = NH_2Cl + OH^- \qquad K > 10^8$$

Chloramine decomposes to nitrogen and ammonia in alkaline solution:

$$3\,NH_2Cl + 3\,OH^- \longrightarrow N_2 + 3\,Cl^- + NH_3 + 3\,H_2O$$

The important reaction of chloramine with ammonia to produce hydrazine is discussed in Sec. 7.4. If a solution of chloramine is acidified, **dichloramine** and **nitrogen trichloride** are formed:

$$H^+ + 2\,NH_2Cl = NHCl_2 + NH_4^+ \qquad K \approx 10^6$$

$$H^+ + 3\,NHCl_2 = 2\,NCl_3 + NH_4^+ \qquad K \approx 10^4$$

Nitrogen trichloride is an explosive, oily liquid which is soluble in solvents such as carbon tetrachloride and benzene.

Nitrosyl chloride (mp, $-64.5°$; bp, $-6.4°$) is an orange-yellow gas which may be prepared by the reaction of chlorine and nitric oxide

$$2\,NO + Cl_2 \longrightarrow 2\,NOCl$$

or by passing N_2O_4 over moist KCl

$$N_2O_4 + KCl \longrightarrow NOCl + KNO_3$$

Nitryl chloride (mp, $-145°$; bp, $-15.9°$) is a colorless gas that can be prepared by the reaction of chlorosulfonic acid with anhydrous nitric acid

$$ClSO_3H + HNO_3 \longrightarrow NO_2Cl + H_2SO_4$$

or by the passage of hydrogen chloride through a solution of nitric acid in sulfuric acid

$$HCl + NO_2^+ + HSO_4^- \longrightarrow NO_2Cl + H_2SO_4$$

(HNO_3 reacts with 2 H_2SO_4 to form $NO_2^+ + H_3O^+ + 2\ HSO_4^-$.) Nitrosyl and nitryl chlorides are both "double acid anhydrides." They react vigorously with water as follows:

$$NOCl + H_2O \longrightarrow HNO_2 + H^+ + Cl^-$$
$$NO_2Cl + H_2O \longrightarrow 2\,H^+ + NO_3^- + Cl^-$$

So-called **nitrogen triiodide**, $NI_3 \cdot NH_3$, is prepared by the reaction of aqueous ammonia with iodine:

$$5\,NH_3 + 3\,I_2 \longrightarrow NI_3 \cdot NH_3(s) + 3\,NH_4^+ + 3\,I^-$$

The black solid is a shock- and light-sensitive compound that decomposes explosively to nitrogen, iodine, and ammonia.

7.4 HYDRAZINE. The overall reaction for the preparation of hydrazine in aqueous solution is:

$$2\,NH_3 + OCl^- \longrightarrow N_2H_4 + Cl^- + H_2O$$

but the reaction proceeds in two main steps. In the first step, chloramine is formed:

$$NH_3 + OCl^- \longrightarrow NH_2Cl + OH^-$$

Then the chloramine reacts with ammonia to form hydrazine:

$$NH_3 + NH_2Cl + OH^- \longrightarrow N_2H_4 + Cl^- + H_2O$$

The latter reaction proceeds by two independent paths, a base-independent path and a base-catalyzed path. The base-independent path is believed to be the nucleophilic attack of ammonia on chloramine:

$$NH_3 + NH_2Cl \longrightarrow N_2H_5^+ + Cl^- \quad \text{(slow)}$$

$$N_2H_5^+ + OH^- \rightleftharpoons N_2H_4 + H_2O \quad \text{(fast)}$$

The base-catalyzed path is believed to involve the preliminary formation of the chloramide ion, followed by attack on this ion by ammonia:

$$NH_2Cl + OH^- \rightleftharpoons NHCl^- + H_2O \quad \text{(fast)}$$

$$NH_3 + NHCl^- \longrightarrow N_2H_4 + Cl^- \quad \text{(slow)}$$

The following side reaction prevents the hydrazine from forming in 100 percent yield:

$$2\,NH_2Cl + N_2H_4 \longrightarrow N_2 + 2\,NH_4^+ + 2\,Cl^-$$

Large excesses of ammonia are usually employed in order to favor the chloramine-ammonia reaction over the chloramine-hydrazine reaction. Gelatin or glue is also added in order to sequester trace amounts of heavy metal ions which somehow catalyze the hydrazine-destroying reaction. Distillation of the resulting dilute solution of hydrazine yields a 58.5 percent hydrazine solution which may be concentrated to anhydrous N_2H_4 by distillation over sodium hydroxide.

Anhydrous hydrazine is a colorless hygroscopic liquid that freezes at $2°$ and boils at $113.5°$. In aqueous solution, it is a somewhat weaker base than ammonia:

$$N_2H_4 + H_2O = N_2H_5^+ + OH^- \qquad K_{25°} = 8.5 \times 10^{-7}$$

In both acidic and alkaline solutions, hydrazine is a strong reducing agent. Some oxidizing agents, such as acid iodate, neutral iodine, and alkaline ferricyanide, oxidize hydrazine to nitrogen. Both nitrogen and ammonia are formed by some oxidizing agents, such as ferric, ceric, and permanganate. Still other oxidizing agents, such as acidic peroxide and nitrous acid, take hydrazine to hydrazoic acid, HN_3.

7.5 HYDROXYLAMINE. Hydroxylamine, NH_2OH, may be prepared by the hydrolysis of primary aliphatic nitro compounds:

$$RCH_2NO_2 + H^+ + H_2O \longrightarrow RCOOH + NH_3OH^+$$

by the platinum-catalyzed hydrogenation of nitric oxide:

$$NO + \tfrac{3}{2}H_2 + H^+ \longrightarrow NH_3OH^+$$

by the reduction of nitric acid at a mercury cathode:

$$6\,e^- + NO_3^- + 8\,H^+ \longrightarrow NH_3OH^+ + 2\,H_2O$$

and by the reaction of nitrous acid with bisulfite:

$$HNO_2 + 2\,HSO_3^- \xrightarrow[\text{neutral soln.}]{0°} HON(SO_3)_2{}^{2-} + H_2O$$

$$HON(SO_3)_2{}^{2-} + H^+ + 2\,H_2O \xrightarrow[H^+]{100°} NH_3OH^+ + 2\,HSO_4^-$$

Hydroxylamine (mp 33°) is very unstable in the pure state, and is usually used in aqueous solutions, where it is a considerably weaker base than ammonia:

$$NH_2OH + H_2O = NH_3OH^+ + OH^- \qquad K_{25°} = 6.6 \times 10^{-9}$$

The weaker basicities of hydroxylamine and hydrazine, compared with ammonia, are not unexpected. These molecules may be looked upon as ammonia molecules in which one of the hydrogen atoms has been replaced by a more electron-attracting group. Because of the reduced electron density on the nitrogen atoms, the attraction for protons is reduced.

In highly acidic solutions, the hydroxylammonium ion is quantitatively oxidized to N_2O by excess ferric ion; at low hydrogen ion concentrations, with excess hydroxylamine, nitrogen is the principal product. Powerful oxidizing agents take hydroxylamine up to nitrate.

7.6 HYDRAZOIC ACID. The salts of hydrazoic acid, HN_3, are called **azides.** Sodium azide may be prepared by the reaction of sodium nitrate with sodium amide, either in the molten state at 175° or in liquid ammonia at 120–140°:

$$3\,NaNH_2 + NaNO_3 \longrightarrow NaN_3 + 3\,NaOH + NH_3$$

Another synthesis involves the reaction of nitrous oxide with sodium amide:

$$2\,NaNH_2 + N_2O \longrightarrow NaN_3 + NaOH + NH_3$$

We have already mentioned that various oxidizing agents oxidize hydrazine to hydrazoic acid:

$$N_2H_5^+ + HNO_2 \longrightarrow HN_3 + H^+ + 2\,H_2O$$

Anhydrous hydrazoic acid is usually prepared by the dropwise addition of sulfuric acid to an alkali-metal azide. (Danger!) The pure acid is a fearfully explosive liquid that boils at 37° and freezes at $-80°$. Azides of heavy metals such as lead, mercury, thallium, and barium explode upon sharp impact; they have been used as detonators.

Aqueous hydrazoic acid is about as strong an acid as acetic acid, $K_{25°} = 1.8 \times 10^{-5}$. Azides are similar in many respects to halides. Thus AgN_3 and $Hg_2(N_3)_2$ are insoluble in water, and the following compounds, analogous to the interhalogens, are known: ClN_3, BrN_3, IN_3, NCN_3. The compound analogous to a halogen molecule, N_3—N_3, is unknown. The azide ion is symmetrical and linear:

$$^-N{=}N^+{=}N^- \leftrightarrow N{\equiv}N^+{-}N^{2-} \leftrightarrow {}^{2-}N{-}^+N{\equiv}N.$$

7.7 NITROGEN OXIDES AND OXY-ACIDS. A wide variety of oxides, oxy-acids, and oxy-anions of nitrogen, corresponding to oxidation states of nitrogen from $+1$ to $+5$, have been characterized. Some of these are listed in Table 7.1; the formulas of the more important species are given in **boldface** type.

Nitrous oxide, N_2O, is readily obtained by the thermal decomposition of substances with the empirical formula $N_2O \cdot xH_2O$ (such as ammonium

Table 7.1   NITROGEN OXIDES AND OXY-ACIDS

Formula	Name	Melting Point (°C)	Boiling Point (°C)	Remarks
N_2O	Nitrous oxide	−90.86	−88.48	Relatively unreactive
$H_2N_2O_2$	Hyponitrous acid			Unstable, weak acid
NH_2NO_2	Nitramide			Unstable, weak acid
NO	Nitric oxide	−163.65	−151.77	Moderately reactive
HNO	Nitroxyl			Unknown except as kinetic intermediate and as salts
$H_2N_2O_3$				Unstable; known in solution and as salts
H_2NO_2	Hydronitrous acid			Explosive sodium salt known
N_2O_3	Dinitrogen trioxide	−111	2	Largely dissociated to NO and NO_2
HNO_2	Nitrous acid			Unstable, but salts stable
HOONO	Peroxynitrous acid			Unstable, but anion stable
N_2O_4	Dinitrogen tetroxide	−11.20	21.15	Colorless; largely dissociated to brown NO_2
NO_2	Nitrogen dioxide			Brown, reactive gas
N_2O_5	Dinitrogen pentoxide	Sublimes at 32.4°		Unstable vapor
HNO_3	Nitric acid	−41.60	83	Strong acid
HNO_4	Peroxynitric acid			Unstable
NO_3				Unstable intermediate

nitrate, hyponitrous acid, and nitramide). The molecule is linear with the two nitrogen atoms adjacent to one another: $\overset{+}{N}\equiv\overset{-}{N}-O \leftrightarrow \overset{-}{N}=\overset{+}{N}=O$ At least two different explanations may be given for the fact that nitrous oxide does not have the structure NON. First, the latter structure involves a greater amount of electrostatic repulsion between adjacent atomic kernels than does the structure NNO. The nitrogen kernel has a charge of $+5$, and the oxygen kernel has a charge of $+6$. The repulsion between two adjacent kernels may be measured by the product of the charges. For NON we have $5 \times 6 + 5 \times 6 = 60$, whereas for NNO we have $5 \times 5 + 5 \times 6 = 55$. Second, the only satisfactory electronic structure for NON involves placing a $+2$ formal charge on the oxygen atom and -1 formal charges on the nitrogen atoms: $\overset{-}{N}=\overset{2+}{O}=\overset{-}{N}$. Not only is a $+2$ formal charge almost unknown for oxygen, but such a distribution of charge contradicts the fact that oxygen is more electronegative than nitrogen.

Compared to the other nitrogen oxides, nitrous oxide is relatively inert. It reacts only slowly with oxidizing and reducing agents. Nitrous oxide decomposes into its elements at an appreciable rate when heated above $600°$.

Hyponitrous acid, $H_2N_2O_2$, is a dibasic acid that has the structure HON=NOH. The ionization constants are $K_1 = 9 \times 10^{-8}$ and $K_2 = 1 \times 10^{-11}$. In solid salts, the hyponitrite ion has the *trans* configuration:

$$\overset{-}{O}\diagdown\underset{\cdot\cdot}{N}=N\overset{\diagup O^-}{\underset{\cdot\cdot}{}}$$

Hyponitrites may be prepared in a variety of ways, including the reduction of nitrite by sodium amalgam:

$$2\,NO_2^- + 4\,Na + 2\,H_2O \longrightarrow N_2O_2^{2-} + 4\,Na^+ + 4\,OH^-$$

White crystals of hyponitrous acid may be obtained by evaporating the solution prepared by treating the silver salt with ethereal hydrogen chloride:

$$Ag_2N_2O_2 + 2\,HCl \longrightarrow 2\,AgCl + H_2N_2O_2$$

The solid decomposes to nitrogen, nitrogen oxides, and water. Aqueous solutions decompose principally to nitrous oxide and water.

Nitramide, NH_2NO_2, is an isomer of hyponitrous acid which is formed by the hydrolysis of the nitrocarbamate ion.

$$O_2CNNO_2^{2-} + 2\,H^+ \longrightarrow NH_2NO_2 + CO_2$$

Nitramide is a weak acid in aqueous solution: $K = 2.6 \times 10^{-7}$. As is the case with hyponitrous acid, nitramide decomposes to nitrous oxide and water in aqueous solution.

Nitric oxide, NO, is manufactured by the atmospheric oxidation of ammonia on catalysts such as platinum gauze at temperatures of about 500°:

$$4\,NH_3 + 5\,O_2 \longrightarrow 4\,NO + 6\,H_2O$$

(In the absence of the catalyst, nitrogen is one of the main products of the oxidation of ammonia.) In the laboratory, nitric oxide may be prepared from aqueous solution by the addition of acid to a solution of nitrite and iodide:

$$2\,NO_2^- + 2\,I^- + 4\,H^+ \longrightarrow 2\,NO + I_2 + 2\,H_2O$$

Although gaseous NO is essentially colorless, in the liquid and solid states NO is blue.

According to simple molecular orbital theory (see Sec. 5.2), nitric oxide has the electronic configuration $KK(s\sigma)^2(s\sigma^*)^2(p\pi)^4(p\sigma)^2(p\pi^*)$, corresponding to a bond order of $2\frac{1}{2}$. Nitric oxide has one more electron than molecular nitrogen has, but since the additional electron is in an antibonding orbital, the bond order is less than that in N_2 by half a unit. The same conclusion may be reached by using Linnett's modification of the Lewis octet theory. If we divide the 11 valence electrons into a group of six with the same spin ($\overset{\times}{\times}N\overset{\times}{\times}O\overset{\times}{\times}$) and a group of five with the opposite spin ($\circ N\overset{\circ}{\circ}O\circ$), we have the resultant structure $\overset{\times}{-}N\overset{\circ}{=}O\overset{\times}{-}$. This structure indicates the existence of one unpaired electron and a bond order of $2\frac{1}{2}$.

It is remarkable that an odd molecule (a molecule possessing an odd number of electrons) like NO shows practically no evidence of dimerization in the gaseous state. However, the very high entropy of vaporization at the boiling point (27.13 eu) indicates that some association takes place in the liquid. And the solid consists of loose dimers which are believed to have the structure shown below:

$$\begin{array}{cc} N\text{---}O & \\ | \quad\quad | & 1.10\ \text{Å} \\ O\text{---}N & \\ \end{array}$$
2.38 Å

Most free radicals dimerize because there is an increase in the total number of bonds upon dimerization. It will be noted that no such increase accompanies the dimerization of 2 NO to O=N—N=O.

Nitric oxide reacts rapidly with oxygen to form brown NO_2:

$$2\,NO + O_2 \longrightarrow 2\,NO_2$$

For this reason, it is often mistakenly concluded that NO_2 is formed in reactions that are carried out in open vessels and that actually involve the initial evolution of only NO. The rate of the oxidation *decreases* with increasing temperature. This unusual behavior is explained by a mechanism involving the equilibrium:

$$2\,NO = N_2O_2$$

preceding the bimolecular rate-determining step:

$$N_2O_2 + O_2 \xrightarrow{\;k\;} 2\,NO_2$$

This mechanism yields the observed rate law:

$$\frac{-d[NO]}{dt} = k\,K[NO]^2[O_2]$$

where K is the equilibrium constant for the preliminary equilibrium. If K decreases with increasing temperature faster than k increases with increasing temperature, then the product kK will decrease with increasing temperature.

Nitric oxide is like carbon monoxide in forming complexes with transition metals. The extra antibonding electron of NO is usually transferred to the metal atom to give the nitrosyl cation, $N\equiv O^+$. Typical complexes are $Fe(CN)_5NO^{2-}$ and $FeNO(H_2O)_5^{2+}$. In some complexes, such as $Co(CN)_5NO^{3-}$, an electron is transferred from the metal to NO to form $O=N^-$.

When an equimolar mixture of NO and NO_2 is condensed, blue N_2O_3 is formed. Spectroscopic data are consistent with the $O=N-NO_2$ structure for N_2O_3. The gaseous reaction:

$$N_2O_3 = NO + NO_2$$

has an equilibrium constant of 2.10 atm at 25°.

Dinitrogen trioxide may be looked upon as the anhydride of **nitrous acid.** It reacts with alkaline solutions to give practically pure nitrite:

$$N_2O_3 + 2\,OH^- \longrightarrow 2\,NO_2^- + H_2O$$

However, when N_2O_3 reacts with liquid water, appreciable amounts of NO, N_2O_4, and nitrate are formed in addition to nitrous acid. In the gaseous state, N_2O_3 (in equilibrium with NO and NO_2) reacts with water to form nitrous acid vapor:

$$NO(g) + NO_2(g) + H_2O(g) = 2\,HNO_2(g)$$

At 25°, the equilibrium constant for the reaction is 1.27 atm^{-1}.

Nitrous acid is a weak acid with an ionization constant of 4.5×10^{-4}; thus aqueous solutions of the acid may be prepared by the addition of a strong acid to a solution of a nitrite. The solutions decompose reversibly at a measurable rate to give nitric oxide and nitrate:

$$3\,HNO_2 = H^+ + NO_3^- + 2\,NO + H_2O$$

The decomposition is believed to proceed by the following mechanism:

$$4\,HNO_2 = N_2O_4 + 2\,NO + 2\,H_2O \quad \text{(rapid, reversible)}$$

$$N_2O_4 \rightarrow NO^+ + NO_3^- \quad \text{(rate-determining)}$$

$$NO^+ + H_2O = HNO_2 + H^+ \quad \text{(rapid, reversible)}$$

Nitrites may be prepared either by thermal decomposition of alkali nitrates or by reduction of nitrates by carbon or lead. The nitrite ion is bent, with an N—O bond distance of 1.24 Å and a bond angle of 115°.

The nitrogen(IV) oxides, N_2O_4 and NO_2, always exist in the presence of one another in the gaseous and liquid states. The reaction:

$$2\,NO_2(g) = N_2O_4(g)$$

rapidly reaches equilibrium; at 25°, $K = 8.8$ atm^{-1}. In the solid state, the material exists as pure N_2O_4. Nitrogen dioxide is brown and paramagnetic; dinitrogen tetroxide is colorless and diamagnetic.

Nitrogen dioxide has a V-shaped structure; the N—O bond distance is 1.19 Å, and the bond angle is 134°. Although the bonding may be described in terms of molecular orbital theory, the following Linnett-type structures provide an octet of electrons around each atom:

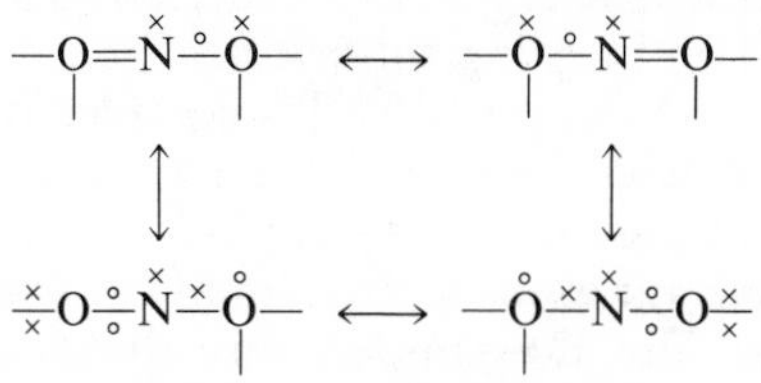

Dinitrogen tetroxide has the structure: O_2N—NO_2. The N—N bond distance, 1.75 Å, is much greater than an ordinary N—N single bond distance. (The N—N distance in hydrazine is 1.47 Å.) This, together with the fact that the O—N—O bond angles in NO_2 and N_2O_4 are the same, suggests that N_2O_4 corresponds to a pair of NO_2 molecules very loosely held together. The chemistry of liquid N_2O_4 suggests that in the pure liquid (as well as in solvents such as sulfuric acid and dimethyl sulfoxide), N_2O_4 self-ionizes to give NO^+ and NO_3^- ions.

Dinitrogen pentoxide, N_2O_5, is a colorless, volatile solid which may be made in either of two ways. In the first way, nitric acid is dehydrated with phosphorus(V) oxide and the N_2O_5 is distilled in a current of ozone and oxygen:

$$2\,HNO_3 + P_2O_5 \longrightarrow \frac{2}{x}(HPO_3)_x + N_2O_5$$

In the second way, N_2O_4 is oxidized with ozone:

$$N_2O_4 + O_3 \longrightarrow N_2O_5 + O_2$$

N_2O_5 is the anhydride of nitric acid; it is deliquescent and reacts with water as follows:

$$N_2O_5 + H_2O \longrightarrow 2\,HNO_3$$

The gaseous molecule probably has the structure $O_2N—O—NO_2$, but solid N_2O_5 consists of an ionic lattice of nitryl ions, NO_2^+, and nitrate ions, NO_3^-.

Nitric acid, HNO_3, is generally made by the absorption in water of NO_2 obtained from the oxidation of ammonia:

$$3\,NO_2(g) + H_2O = 2\,H^+ + 2\,NO_3^- + NO(g)$$

The reaction with water is initially rapid, but as the concentration of nitric acid builds up, it becomes very slow, largely because the equilibrium pressure of nitric oxide becomes very great. Therefore, in order to prepare acid of concentration greater than 50 percent, a mixture of NO_2 and oxygen is passed into water, the oxygen serving to oxidize the NO formed in the reaction. The 68.4 percent acid is a constant-boiling mixture with a boiling point of 122°. Anhydrous nitric acid is prepared by distillation of a mixture of aqueous nitric acid and fuming sulfuric acid.

In dilute aqueous solutions nitric acid is completely ionized and is considered to be a strong acid. However, Raman spectra of nitric acid solutions indicate that ionization is incomplete at concentrations as low as 3 M and that at higher concentrations a large fraction of the acid is in the form of HNO_3 molecules. The Raman-determined value for the ionization constant of nitric acid is $K = 21$. In nonaqueous solvents of low dielectric constant, such as acetic acid, nitric acid has been shown to be a much weaker acid than other "strong" acids such as $HClO_4$, HBr, H_2SO_4, and HCl.

Nitric acid is an oxidizing agent, for which the rate of reduction and the reduction products are strongly influenced by its concentration. Thus in solutions that are less than 1 M in concentration, iodine is formed very slowly from iodide solutions; whereas at concentrations greater than 2 M, iodine, bromine, and even chlorine are rapidly liberated from halide salts. At low concentrations the principal reduction product of nitric acid is NO, whereas at higher concentrations considerable amounts of NO_2 are evolved. The metals gold, platinum, rhodium, and iridium are not attacked by hot concentrated nitric acid. But these metals may be dissolved by **aqua**

regia, which is a mixture of three parts of concentrated HCl and one part of concentrated HNO_3. The effectiveness of aqua regia is due in part to the presence of both chlorine and nitrosyl chloride

$$4 H^+ + NO_3^- + 3 Cl^- = NOCl + Cl_2 + 2 H_2O$$

and in part to the complexing ability of the chloride ion, which forms species such as $AuCl_4^-$ with the dissolved metal ions.

Solutions of nitric acid in concentrated sulfuric acid have no appreciable vapor pressure at ordinary temperatures, and freezing-point depression studies show that each mole of nitric acid dissolves to give four moles of species. The following reaction is believed to take place:

$$HONO_2 + 2 H_2SO_4 = NO_2^+ + H_3O^+ + 2 HSO_4^-$$

The **nitryl ion,** NO_2^+, has been identified in such solutions by Raman spectroscopy. The solutions are commonly used by organic chemists for the nitration of aromatic compounds such as benzene. The net reaction may be written:

$$C_6H_6 + NO_2^+ + HSO_4^- \longrightarrow C_6H_5NO_2 + H_2SO_4$$

The structure of the gaseous HNO_3 molecule is as follows:

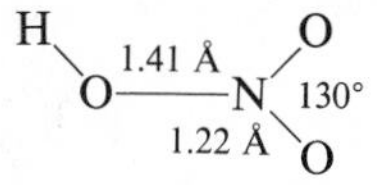

$$
\begin{array}{c}
H \\
\diagdown \quad 1.41\ \text{Å} \quad \diagup O \\
O \underline{\qquad} N\ \ 130° \\
1.22\ \text{Å} \diagdown O
\end{array}
$$

The nitrogen atom and oxygen atoms are coplanar. The nitrate ion is planar, the three oxygens occupying the corners of an equilateral triangle. The NO bond distance is 1.22 Å. The ion may be considered a resonance hybrid of three structures:

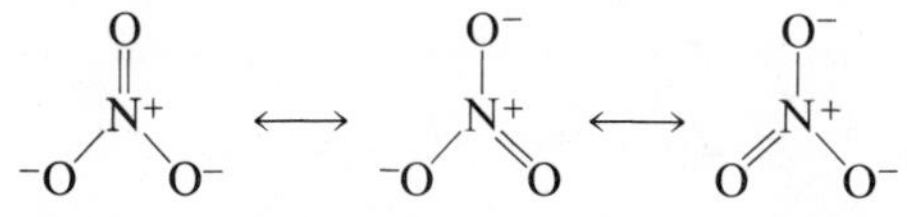

$$
\begin{array}{ccc}
\begin{array}{c} O \\ \| \\ N^+ \\ {}^-O \quad O^- \end{array} & \longleftrightarrow & \begin{array}{c} O^- \\ | \\ N^+ \\ {}^-O \quad O \end{array} & \longleftrightarrow & \begin{array}{c} O^- \\ | \\ N^+ \\ O \quad O^- \end{array}
\end{array}
$$

7.8 ANALYSIS. **Ammonia** and **ammonium salts** may be identified by the addition of a concentrated solution of a strong base; the volatilized ammonia is detected by its odor or by its action on a piece of moist red litmus paper. Ammonia may be quantitatively expelled from a solution containing strong base by distillation; the ammonia may be absorbed in a known excess of standard acid, and the excess acid back-titrated with base using methyl red indicator.

Hydrazine may be detected by its reaction with salicylaldehyde to form a precipitate of salicylaldazine:

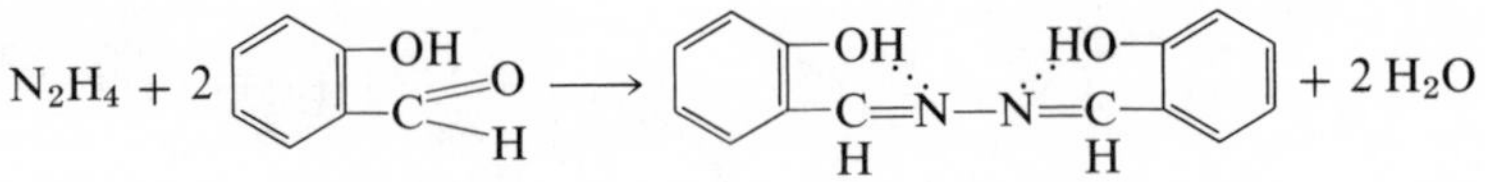

$$N_2H_4 + 2 \quad \text{[salicylaldehyde structure]} \longrightarrow \text{[salicylaldazine structure]} + 2\,H_2O$$

Hydrazine is quantitatively determined by titration with standard iodate solution in 6 M HCl:

$$N_2H_4 + IO_3^- + 2\,H^+ + 2\,Cl^- \longrightarrow N_2 + ICl_2^- + 3\,H_2O$$

The iodate is first reduced to iodine, which subsequently is oxidized to the dichloroiodate(I) ion.

Hydroxylamine reacts with salicylaldehyde to form salicylaldoxime, which, in the presence of cupric ions, forms an insoluble yellow copper complex:

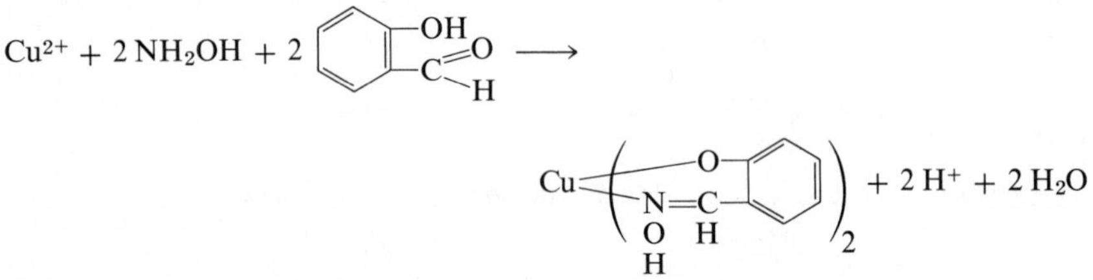

$$Cu^{2+} + 2\,NH_2OH + 2 \quad \text{[salicylaldehyde structure]} \longrightarrow$$

$$\text{[copper complex structure]} + 2\,H^+ + 2\,H_2O$$

Hydroxylamine may be quantitatively oxidized to nitrate by excess standard bromate in strongly acidic solutions:

$$5\,NH_3OH^+ + 6\,BrO_3^- \longrightarrow 5\,NO_3^- + 3\,Br_2 + 4\,H^+ + 8\,H_2O$$

The excess oxidizing agent is determined by adding iodide and titrating the liberated triiodide with thiosulfate.

Nitrite reacts with excess ferrous ion in dilute acid to form the dark brown $FeNO^{2+}$ ion:

$$2\,Fe^{2+} + HNO_2 + H^+ \longrightarrow FeNO^{2+} + Fe^{3+} + H_2O$$

The corresponding reduction of nitrate takes place only in strongly acidic solutions. Nitrite is quantitatively determined by oxidation to nitrate by an excess of standard oxidizing agent (permanganate or ceric ion) followed by back-titration with standard ferrous solution.

The reduction of **nitrate** to $FeNO^{2+}$ by ferrous ion is the basis of the well-known "brown ring" test for nitrate. The test is usually carried out by slowly adding concentrated sulfuric acid to an inclined test tube containing a mixture of the unknown solution and a ferrous sulfate solution. A brown ring at the interface between the upper dilute solution and the denser sulfuric acid indicates the presence of nitrate. Nitrite interferes with the test, but it may be destroyed beforehand by treatment with sulfamic acid:

$$HOSO_2NH_2 + NO_2^- \longrightarrow N_2 + HSO_4^- + H_2O$$

Nitrate may be analyzed quantitatively by reduction with aluminum in alkaline solution to ammonia, and determination of the ammonia as described above:

$$3\,NO_3^- + 8\,Al + 5\,OH^- + 34\,H_2O \longrightarrow 8\,Al(H_2O)_2(OH)_4^- + 3\,NH_3$$

The latter reaction also may be used for the qualitative analysis of nitrite and nitrate in the presence of highly colored species which would mask the $FeNO^{2+}$ color.

SUGGESTED REFERENCES

Audrieth, L. F. and J. Kleinberg, chapters on liquid ammonia in *Non-Aqueous Solvents.* New York: Wiley, 1953.

Jolly, W. L., *The Inorganic Chemistry of Nitrogen.* New York: Benjamin, 1964.

Lepoutre, G. and M. J. Sienko, *Metal-Ammonia Solutions; Physicochemical Properties.* New York: Benjamin, 1964.

Yost, D. M. and H. Russell, Jr., *Systematic Inorganic Chemistry.* Englewood Cliffs, N.J.: Prentice Hall, 1946.

8

Phosphorus

and Arsenic

8.1 OCCURRENCE. Phosphorus constitutes about 0.1 percent of the earth's crust and exists principally in various orthophosphate minerals such as $Ca_3(PO_4)_2$ and the apatites $Ca_5F(PO_4)_3$ and $Ca_5Cl(PO_4)_3$. Most of the phosphate mined is converted to fertilizers; almost all the rest is used in the production of elementary phosphorus which is converted to various phosphorus compounds. Calcium phosphate is the principal constituent of bones and teeth, and many proteins contain phosphorus.

Arsenic constitutes about 5×10^{-4} percent of the earth's crust and exists principally in the form of sulfide minerals such as arsenical pyrites, $FeAsS$; orpiment, As_2S_3, and realgar, As_4S_4. Some arsenic exists as the oxide claudetite, As_2O_3, and as the arsenides $FeAs_2$, $CoAs_2$, and $NiAs$.

8.2 THE ELEMENTS. Phosphorus vapor, containing P_4 molecules, is prepared by heating phosphate minerals with coke and silica in an electric furnace:

$$2\,Ca_3(PO_4)_2 + 6\,SiO_2 + 10\,C \longrightarrow$$
$$P_4 + 6\,CaSiO_3 + 10\,CO$$

The phosphorus is condensed under water as **white phosphorus,** which consists of a lattice of P_4 molecules. In

88

the P_4 molecule, the phosphorus atoms form the corners of a regular tetra-hedron; each atom is directly bonded to the other three atoms. The P—P—P bond angle of 60° in P_4 is much lower than the 90° angle favorable for the use of pure p atomic orbitals. Thus it is understandable that white phosphorus is unstable with respect to **red phosphorus**—a name that encompasses several modifications of phosphorus in which phosphorus atoms are linked together into random chains or networks in which the P—P—P bond angles are presumably much greater than in the P_4 molecule. The conversion of white phosphorus to red phosphorus is effected by heating, by exposure to light, and by treatment with iodine. The third main modification of phosphorus, even more stable than red phosphorus, is **black phosphorus.** Crystalline black phosphorus is prepared by heating white phosphorus under high pressure or in the presence of mercury as a catalyst with a "seed" crystal of black phosphorus. The crystal structure consists of corrugated sheets of phosphorus atoms.

As might be expected, white phosphorus is much more reactive, more soluble, and has a higher vapor pressure than the other modifications of phosphorus. White phosphorus inflames in air, and therefore it is generally stored under water. Its solubility in carbon disulfide is 880 g per 100 g of solvent at 10°. The red and black varieties of phosphorus are unreactive in air at ordinary temperatures, and they are not appreciably soluble in carbon disulfide or other solvents. White phosphorus melts at 44.1° and boils at 280.5°. Red phosphorus melts at approximately 590° and sublimes at one atmosphere pressure around 430°. For the conversion of white phosphorus to red phosphorus, $P_{4(s)} = 4 P_{(red)}$, $\Delta H°_{25°} = -17.6$ kcal/mole and $\Delta F°_{25°} = -13.2$ kcal/mole.

Arsenic is prepared by the reduction of arsenic(III) oxide with carbon or hydrogen:

$$As_2O_3 + 3 C \longrightarrow 2 As + 3 CO$$

$$As_2O_3 + 6 H_2 \longrightarrow 2 As + 3 H_2O$$

Sulfide ores are first roasted (heated in air) to the oxide; for example:

$$2 As_2S_3 + 9 O_2 \longrightarrow 2 As_2O_3 + 6 SO_2$$

Usually elementary arsenic exists in the so-called **metallic form,** which has a crystal structure similar to that of black phosphorus. This modification of arsenic is a good thermal conductor, but a poor electrical conductor; it readily sublimes to form shiny grey crystals. A very finely divided, black form of metallic arsenic may be prepared by the reduction of arsenious acid with stannous ion:

$$2 H_3AsO_3 + 3 Sn^{2+} + 6 H^+ \longrightarrow 2 As + 3 Sn^{4+} + 6 H_2O$$

The element sublimes at 1 atm pressure at 613°; the melting point (under 36 atm pressure) is 817°. Arsenic exists in the vapor as As_4 molecules, and by rapidly quenching the vapor at low temperatures, **yellow arsenic** may be prepared. This modification of arsenic is probably analogous in structure to white phosphorus; it rapidly converts to the metallic form at room temperature.

8.3 PHOSPHIDES AND ARSENIDES. Almost all the metals in the Periodic Table form binary compounds with phosphorus and arsenic. Most metals form more than one phosphide. Thus nickel forms NiP, NiP_2, Ni_6P_5, Ni_2P, Ni_5P_2, and Ni_3P. The metal phosphides and arsenides are usually prepared by direct reaction of the elements or by the thermal decomposition of one compound into another with loss of phosphorus or arsenic.

All the alkali metals form phosphides of formula M_2P_5, and lithium and sodium form compounds of composition M_3P. Lithium, sodium, and potassium form arsenides of formula M_3As. All these compounds react with water to produce either phosphine, PH_3, or arsine, AsH_3. The M_3P and M_3As compounds are probably best looked upon as salts of these latter hydrides. The alkaline-earth metals form phosphides and arsenides with the formulas M_3P_2 and M_3As_2, which hydrolyze to give phosphine and arsine, respectively. The phosphides and arsenides of the elements of Group 3b (BP, AlP, GaP, InP, BAs, $AlAs$, $GaAs$, and $InAs$) are interesting because they all have the same "zinc blende" crystal structure which is similar to that of elementary silicon. In these compounds, each atom is bonded to four atoms of a different kind, presumably by the use of sp^3 hybrid orbitals, and each atom has an octet of valence electrons. Except for $InAs$, which melts at $943°$, all these compounds melt above $1000°$. Like silicon, these compounds are semiconductors and, depending on the kind of impurities, can be n- or p-conducting. (See Sec. 10.2.) Phosphides and arsenides of transition metals, such as Fe_2P and $NiAs$, are often metallic-appearing and conduct electricity.

8.4 HYDRIDES. We have already pointed out that phosphides and arsenides of the electropositive metals undergo hydrolysis to give the poisonous gases **phosphine,** PH_3, and **arsine,** AsH_3. These hydrides may also be prepared by the reduction of the appropriate trichlorides with lithium aluminum hydride in ether solvents:

$$4\,MCl_3 + 3\,LiAlH_4 \longrightarrow 4\,MH_3 + 3\,LiCl + 3\,AlCl_3$$

Phosphine may be conveniently prepared by heating anhydrous phosphorous acid to about $200°$:

$$4\,H_3PO_3 \longrightarrow 3\,H_3PO_4 + PH_3$$

Arsine may be conveniently prepared by the addition of an alkaline aqueous solution of arsenite and hydroborate to acid:

$$4\,H_2AsO_3^- + 3\,BH_4^- + 7\,H^+ \longrightarrow 4\,AsH_3 + 3\,B(OH)_3 + 3\,H_2O$$

The hydrides **diphosphine** and **diarsine**, P_2H_4 and As_2H_4, respectively, are obtained in small yields as by-products of the above syntheses.

Some physical properties of the hydrides are summarized in Table 8.1. Both phosphine and arsine are pyramidal molecules with bond angles (HPH, 93.5°; HAsH, 91.8°) much smaller than the 106.8° HNH angle in ammonia. The bond angles indicate the use of essentially pure p orbitals in the bonding. The bonding pairs of electrons in these hydrides apparently do not repel each other as strongly as they do in the smaller ammonia molecule. Because the lone pair electrons in phosphine and arsine occupy almost pure s orbitals, these electrons are held fairly tightly and do not project out from the molecules. Consequently, phosphine and arsine are very weak bases. Thus phosphine has essentially the same solubility in 1 M HCl as it does in pure water, but, under anhydrous conditions, easily dissociated **phosphonium salts** such as PH_4Cl can be formed. In liquid ammonia, both phosphine and arsine show their acid character by reacting with the amide ion or the electron:

$$NH_2^- + PH_3 \longrightarrow PH_2^- + NH_3$$

$$e^- + AsH_3 \longrightarrow AsH_2^- + \tfrac{1}{2} H_2$$

Alkali and alkaline-earth metal salts such as $KAsH_2$ and $[Ca(NH_3)_6](PH_2)_2$ may be isolated. The anions are completely hydrolyzed to the corresponding hydrides in water. Indirect evidence for both the acidity and basicity of phosphine in water has been obtained from a study of the exchange of hydrogen between heavy water and phosphine. The exchange reaction is catalyzed by both acid and base, and the following mechanisms seem likely:

Acid catalysis:

$$D_3O^+ + PH_3 \longrightarrow PH_3D^+ + D_2O \quad \text{(slow)}$$

$$PH_3D^+ + D_2O \longrightarrow PH_2D + HD_2O^+ \quad \text{(fast)}$$

Base catalysis:

$$OD^- + PH_3 \longrightarrow PH_2^- + HOD \quad \text{(slow)}$$

$$PH_2^- + D_2O \longrightarrow PH_2D + OD^- \quad \text{(fast)}$$

Table 8.1   SOME PHYSICAL PROPERTIES OF THE HYDRIDES OF PHOSPHORUS AND ARSENIC

	PH_3	P_2H_4	AsH_3	As_2H_4
Melting point, °C	−133.78	—	−116.93	—
Boiling point, °C	−87.74	63.5	−62.48	~100
Heat of formation of gas at 25°, kcal/mole	1.3	5.0	15.9	—

By measuring the rate constants for the slow steps, and by assuming the rates of the fast steps to be equal to the rates at which the species collide, the following equilibrium constants have been estimated:

$$PH_3 + H_2O = PH_4^+ + OH^- \qquad K_{27°} \approx 4 \times 10^{-28}$$

$$PH_3 + H_2O = H_3O^+ + PH_2^- \qquad K_{27°} \approx 1.6 \times 10^{-29}$$

Both phosphine and arsine are powerful reducing agents. (See Tables 8.3 and 8.5.) Diphosphine and diarsine readily decompose to the mono-hydrides and nonvolatile, polymeric hydrides:

$$5\,M_2H_4 \longrightarrow 6\,MH_3 + 2/x(M_2H)_x$$

8.5 HALIDES AND OXYHALIDES. There are two main types of halides: the trihalides, MX_3, and the pentahalides, MX_5. All possible binary trihalides of phosphorus and arsenic have been prepared; their physical properties are given in Tables 3.3 and 4.5. No pentaiodide of phosphorus is known, and the only known pentahalide of arsenic is the fluoride. For each of the pentahalides, a corresponding oxyhalide, MOX_3, is known. Some physical properties of the pentahalides and oxyhalides are presented in Table 8.2.

All the binary halides except PF_3 can be formed by the direct halogenation of the elements: the trihalides are obtained with excess phosphorus or arsenic, and the pentahalides are obtained with excess halogen. **Phosphorus trifluoride** may be prepared by a halogen exchange reaction between PCl_3 and AsF_3 or SbF_3:

$$PCl_3 + AsF_3 \longrightarrow PF_3 + AsCl_3$$

Most of the driving force for this reaction probably is due to the high volatility of PF_3. **Phosphorus(V) oxychloride,** usually called **phosphoryl**

Table 8.2   PROPERTIES OF THE PHOSPHORUS(V)
AND ARSENIC(V) HALIDES AND OXYHALIDES

	Melting Point (°C)	Boiling Point (°C)
PF_5	−93.7	−84.5
PCl_5	167	160 (subl)
PBr_5	<100 (dec)	106 (dec)
POF_3	−68	−39.7
$POCl_3$	1.1	105.8
$POBr_3$	55	191.7
AsF_5	−79.8	−53.2
$AsOF_3$	−68	26

chloride, may be prepared by the action of various oxidizing agents on PCl_3 or by the reaction of P_4O_{10} with the pentachloride:

$$O_2 + 2\,PCl_3 \longrightarrow 2\,POCl_3$$

$$P_4O_{10} + 6\,PCl_5 \longrightarrow 10\,POCl_3$$

The trihalides are pyramidal, with approximately tetrahedral X—M—X bond angles; the pentahalides are trigonal bipyramidal in the vapor state, and the oxyhalides are approximately tetrahedral. (See Fig. 8.1.) In the trihalides and oxyhalides, the orbitals used for bonding by the central atom may be fairly accurately described as sp^3 hybrid orbitals. In the case of the pentahalides, we may consider the "equatorial" halogen atoms (those which form an equilateral triangle, with the phosphorus or arsenic atom in the center) to be bonded by the use of sp^2 hybrid orbitals from the central atom, and the two "axial" halogen atoms to be bonded by the one remaining p orbital of the central atom. Because only one low-energy orbital is available for the formation of two axial bonds*, the axial bonds are relatively weak and have considerable ionic character. The molecules may be considered resonance hybrids of the structures:

$$\begin{array}{cc} X^- & X \\[2pt] \overset{\displaystyle X}{\underset{\displaystyle X}{\diagdown}}M^+\!\!-\!X & \overset{\displaystyle X}{\underset{\displaystyle X}{\diagdown}}M^+\!\!-\!X \\[2pt] X & X^- \end{array}$$

The observed bond distances in the pentahalides are consistent with this bonding description. Thus, in PCl_5, the axial P—Cl distance is 2.19 Å, and the equatorial P—Cl distance is 2.04 Å. The pentahalides of phosphorus

---

* A small but significant contribution to the axial bonding is made by the $3d$ orbitals of phosphorus and the $4d$ orbitals of arsenic. Thus the axial orbitals may be looked upon as pd hybrid orbitals. However, we may here neglect this d orbital contribution because it is not necessary to an understanding of the structure.

FIGURE 8.1   *Bonding in the phosphorus halides and oxyhalides.*

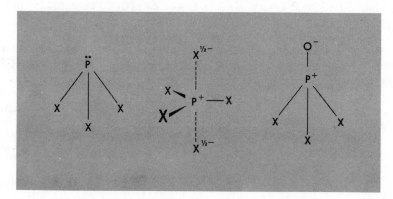

and arsenic are just a few of many examples of nonmetallic compounds in which a central atom has apparently exceeded an octet of valence electrons. XeF_4, SF_6, I_3^-, and BrF_5 are other examples. In all such cases, however, the octet theory can remain inviolate if we describe the bonding in terms of split p orbitals, much as we have done above.

In the solid state, **PCl₅** consists of an ionic lattice of tetrahedral PCl_4^+ ions and octahedral PCl_6^- ions. It is interesting that solid **PBr₅** is different; it consists of a lattice of PBr_4^+ and Br^- ions. Obviously, bromine atoms are too big for six of them to fit comfortably around a phosphorus atom.

The reactions of the phosphorus trihalides with water and ammonia are discussed in Sec. 8.6 and 8.9. The trihalides of phosphorus and arsenic are Lewis bases. Some typical reactions demonstrating their basic character are as follows:

$$PCl_3 + BBr_3 \longrightarrow \overset{+}{Cl_3}P-\overset{-}{BBr_3}$$

$$4\,PCl_3 + Ni(CO)_4 \longrightarrow 4\,CO + Ni(PCl_3)_4$$

$$AsF_3 + F^- \longrightarrow AsF_4^-$$

Both **PF₅** and **AsF₅** react with metal fluorides to form **hexafluorophosphates** and **hexafluoroarsenates,** respectively. With certain acidic halides, PCl_5 forms adducts which are probably ionic; thus **PCl₅·BCl₃** is probably better formulated as $[PCl_4^+][BCl_4^-]$. AsF_3 reacts with chlorine to form a solid of empirical composition **AsF₃Cl₂;** because the compound dissolves in liquid AsF_3, increasing the electrical conductivity, it probably has the structure $[AsCl_4^+][AsF_6^-]$. Both phosphorus pentachloride and phosphoryl chloride react vigorously with water to give orthophosphoric acid:

$$PCl_5 + 4\,H_2O \longrightarrow H_3PO_4 + 5\,H^+ + 5\,Cl^-$$

$$POCl_3 + 3\,H_2O \longrightarrow H_3PO_4 + 3\,H^+ + 3\,Cl^-$$

The reaction of $POCl_3$ with ammonia is discussed in Sec. 8.9.

Diphosphorus tetrachloride, P_2Cl_4 (mp $-28°$, bp $\sim 140°$), is prepared by the action of an electric discharge on a mixture of PCl_3 and a reducing agent such as hydrogen, phosphorus, or zinc. The compound decomposes slowly at room temperature to give PCl_3 and $(PCl)_x$. In contrast, the corresponding iodide, P_2I_4 (mp $124.5°$), is stable at room temperature and may be prepared by direct reaction of the elements.

8.6 OXIDES AND OXYACIDS OF PHOSPHORUS. The important oxyacids of phosphorus are **hypophosphorous acid,** H_3PO_2; **phosphorous acid,** H_3PO_3; and **orthophosphoric acid,** H_3PO_4. Oxidation potential diagrams involving these species (or their anions), phosphorus, and phosphine are presented on the next page. Notice that all the potentials are very positive. Even very weak oxidizing agents will oxidize phosphine, phosphorus, and hypophosphorous acid up to phosphorous acid. However, the last step, from phosphorous acid to phosphoric acid, is more difficult than would have

Acidic Solutions:

$$PH_3 \xrightarrow{\ 0.05\ } P_4 \xrightarrow{\ 0.51\ } H_3PO_2 \xrightarrow{\ 0.50\ } H_3PO_3 \xrightarrow{\ 0.28\ } H_3PO_4$$

0.16

0.28

Basic Solutions:

$$PH_3 \xrightarrow{\ 0.89\ } P_4 \xrightarrow{\ 2.05\ } H_2PO_2^- \xrightarrow{\ 1.57\ } HPO_3^{2-} \xrightarrow{\ 1.12\ } PO_4^{3-}$$

1.18

1.31

been anticipated from the potential; an oxidizing agent about as strong as iodine is required. It is also remarkable that all the intermediate oxidation states (except the $+3$ state in basic solutions) are unstable with respect to disproportionation.

The disproportionation of phosphorus in hot alkaline solutions serves as a source of **hypophosphite:**

$$P_4 + 3\,OH^- + 3\,H_2O \longrightarrow 3\,H_2PO_2^- + PH_3$$

Hypophosphorous acid is a monoprotonic acid ($K_{25°} = 8 \times 10^{-2}$) having the structure:

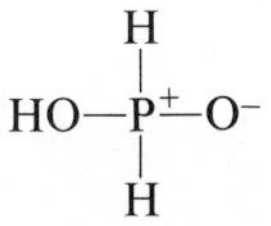

$$\begin{array}{c} H \\ | \\ HO{-}\overset{}{\underset{|}{P}}{\pm}{-}O^- \\ | \\ H \end{array}$$

The two hydrogen atoms directly bound to the phosphorus atom are so firmly bound that they are not exchanged in D_2O solutions. Hot solutions of the acid decompose by disproportionation and by reduction of the water:

$$3\,H_3PO_2 \longrightarrow PH_3 + 2\,H_3PO_3$$

$$H_3PO_2 + H_2O \longrightarrow H_3PO_3 + H_2$$

Phosphorus(III) oxide, P_4O_6, is a white solid (mp 23.8°, bp 175°) which is formed in impure form by the slow combustion of phosphorus in a limited supply of oxygen. A better synthesis is achieved in the low-pressure reaction of phosphorus vapor with nitrous oxide at 600°:

$$6\,N_2O + P_4 \longrightarrow P_4O_6 + 6\,N_2$$

The phosphorus(III) oxide molecule has the structure shown in Fig. 8.2. The oxide reacts with cold water to form **phosphorous acid,** but the reaction does not appear to be reversible:

$$P_4O_6 + 6\,H_2O \longrightarrow 4\,H_3PO_3$$

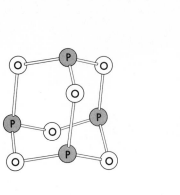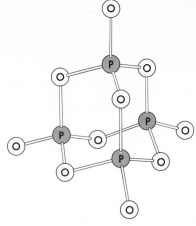

FIGURE 8.2   *The structures of P_4O_6 and P_4O_{10}.*

Phosphorous acid is also prepared by the hydrolysis of PCl_3:

$$PCl_3 + 3\,H_2O \longrightarrow H_3PO_3 + 3\,H^+ + 3\,Cl^-$$

The solid acid (mp 70.1°) may be crystallized from solution. The acid is diprotonic $(K_1(18°) = 5.1 \times 10^{-2},\ \ K_2(18°) = 1.8 \times 10^{-7})$ and has the structure

$$\begin{array}{c} H \\ | \\ HO-\overset{+}{P}{}^{\pm}-O^- \\ | \\ O \\ H \end{array}$$

We have already discussed the disproportionation of the acid to phosphine and phosphoric acid.

When phosphorus is burned in an excess of oxygen, **phosphorus(V) oxide** (often called phosphorus pentoxide after the empirical formula, P_2O_5) is formed. The compound exists in three crystalline modifications. The commonest modification, with hexagonal crystal form, is obtained by condensation of the vapor and consists of P_4O_{10} molecules with the structure shown in Fig. 8.2. This form of the oxide sublimes at 360° (1 atm) and, when heated under pressure at higher temperatures, is converted to the other two modifications, which have orthorhombic form. The orthorhombic forms have infinite layer structures in which each phosphorus atom, as in P_4O_{10}, is bonded to four oxygen atoms, three of which are shared with other phosphorus atoms.

P_4O_{10} is a very efficient desiccant; it reacts vigorously with water to form phosphoric acids. With an excess of water, the principal product is **ortho-phosphoric acid,** H_3PO_4. The acid is triprotonic; at 25°, $K_1 = 7.1 \times 10^{-3}$, $K_2 = 8.0 \times 10^{-8}$ and $K_3 = 5 \times 10^{-13}$. With smaller amounts of water, solutions are obtained which contain various **polyphosphoric acids,** the proportions of which depend on the P_2O_5/H_2O ratio. In Fig. 8.3, the molecular composition of liquid phosphoric acids is plotted as a function of the P_2O_5/H_2O ratio. The structures of orthophosphoric acid, **diphosphoric acid, $H_4P_2O_7$,** and **triphosphoric acid, $H_5P_3O_{10}$,** are as follows:

$$
\begin{array}{ccc}
\text{O}^- & \text{O}^- \quad\quad \text{O}^- & \text{O}^- \quad\quad \text{O}^- \quad\quad \text{O}^- \\
| & | \quad\quad | & | \quad\quad | \quad\quad | \\
\text{HO--P}^{\pm}\text{--OH} & \text{HO--P}^{\pm}\text{--O--P}^{\pm}\text{--OH} & \text{HO--P}^{\pm}\text{--O--P}^{\pm}\text{--O--P}^{\pm}\text{--OH} \\
| & | \quad\quad | & | \quad\quad | \quad\quad | \\
\text{O} & \text{O} \quad\quad \text{O} & \text{O} \quad\quad \text{O} \quad\quad \text{O} \\
\text{H} & \text{H} \quad\quad \text{H} & \text{H} \quad\quad \text{H} \quad\quad \text{H}
\end{array}
$$

In all the polyphosphoric acids and polyphosphates, the phosphorus atoms are surrounded by tetrahedra of oxygen atoms. These PO_4 tetrahedra are linked together by the sharing of oxygen atoms to form chains.

Thus the polyphosphoric acids constitute a homologous series with the generic formula $H_{n+2}P_nO_{3n+1}$. Alkali metal polyphosphates may be prepared by fusion of the appropriate orthophosphates or mixtures of orthophosphates:

$$2\,Na_2HPO_4 \longrightarrow Na_4P_2O_7 + H_2O$$

$$2\,Na_2HPO_4 + NaH_2PO_4 \longrightarrow Na_5P_3O_{10} + 2\,H_2O$$

Attempts to prepare higher members of the series by such condensation reactions result in mixtures. The dehydration of NaH_2PO_4 yields the so-called sodium metaphosphate:

$$NaH_2PO_4 \longrightarrow \frac{1}{x}(NaPO_3)_x + H_2O$$

FIGURE 8.3 *The molecular composition of phosphoric acid as a function of the P_2O_5/H_2O ratio.*

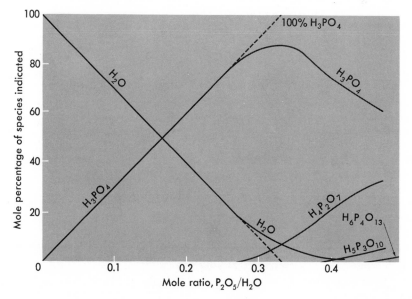

The constitution of the product depends greatly on its thermal history, but generally the material is a complex mixture of both high molecular weight chain polyphosphates and **cyclic metaphosphates.** The best characterized of the cyclic metaphosphates are the **trimetaphosphate** and **tetrametaphosphate,** the structures of which are as follows:

The corresponding metaphosphoric acids constitute a homologous series with the generic formula $(HPO_3)_x$. The various chain and cyclic phosphates may be partially separated from one another by paper chromatography. In this process, a drop of a solution of the mixture is allowed to evaporate on one corner of a sheet of absorbent paper. One edge of the sheet is placed in a bath of solvent, and the solvent slowly moves across the paper, carrying the various phosphates at different rates, depending on their solubilities in the solvent. After this separation, the paper is dried,

FIGURE 8.4   *Corner of a two-dimensional paper chromatogram showing the positions of the pentameta- through octametaphosphate rings in relation to the positions of the well-known ring and chain phosphates. The basic solvent moved 9 inches in 24 hours, whereas the acid solvent moved 4.5 inches in 5.5 hours. From J. Van Wazer,* Phosphorus and Its Compounds, *Vol. I, Fig. 11-7 (New York: John Wiley & Sons, Inc., Interscience, 1958).*

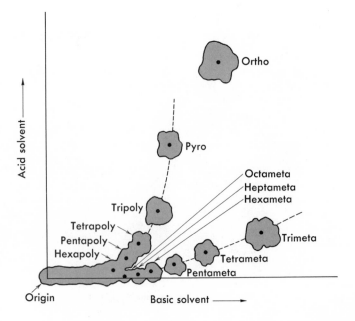

and, if desired, further separation can be achieved by allowing a second solvent to move across the paper at a right angle to the first direction. Finally, the various spots of separated phosphates are made visible by spraying the paper with a reagent, such as molybdate, which gives a color with phosphates. A paper chromatogram such as that described is shown in Fig. 8.4.

Sodium trimetaphosphate, $Na_3(P_3O_9)$, is the principal product when a sodium metaphosphate melt is held at 500–550° for about 12 hours. The dihydrogen tetrametaphosphate ion may be readily prepared free of other phosphates by heating an equimolar mixture of sodium dihydrogenphosphate and orthophosphoric acid to 400°:

$$2\,NaH_2PO_4 + 2\,H_3PO_4 \longrightarrow Na_2H_2P_4O_{12} + 4\,H_2O$$

Tetrametaphosphoric acid may be obtained in approximately 75 percent yields by the hydrolysis of P_4O_{10} in ice water. Presumably the reaction proceeds by the hydrolytic cleavage of two P—O—P bonds in the P_4O_{10} molecule:

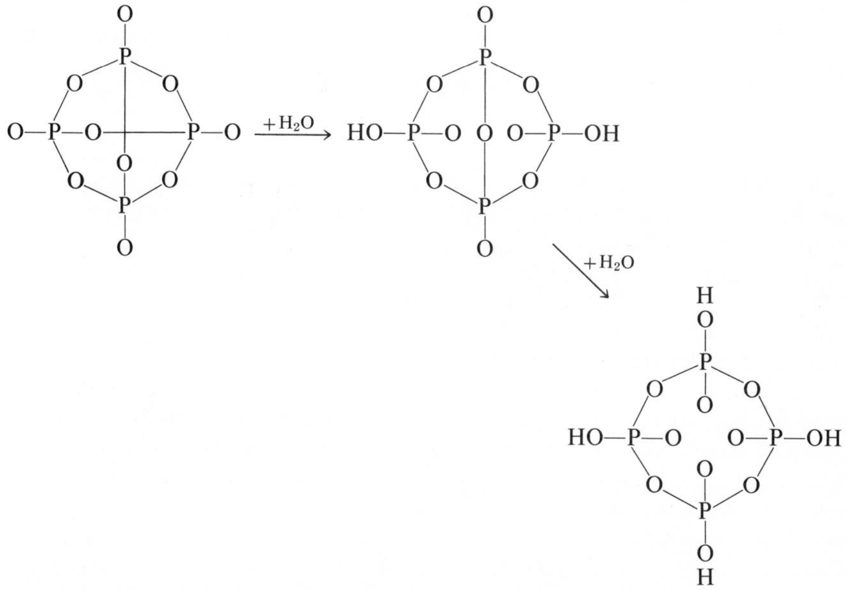

The further hydrolysis to the chain tetraphosphoric acid is slow.

The polyphosphates and (to a lesser extent) the metaphosphates form complexes with metal ions in aqueous solutions. The alkaline-earth metal ions are complexed much more strongly than the alkali metal ions; consequently, sodium polyphosphates find considerable application as water-softeners.

Several relatively unimportant oxyacids of phosphorus, corresponding to lower oxidation states, are known. A salt of composition $Na_3HP_2O_5 \cdot$ $12\,H_2O$ has been prepared by the hydrolysis of PBr_3 in cold aqueous $NaHCO_3$. The anion has the structure

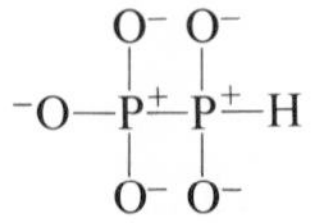

$$\begin{array}{c} \quad O^- \;\; O^- \\ \quad | \quad\; | \\ {}^-O-\overset{+}{P}-\overset{+}{P}-H \\ \quad | \quad\; | \\ \quad O^- \;\; O^- \end{array}$$

The oxidation of red phosphorus by hypochlorite yields the dihydrogen hypophosphate ion, $H_2P_2O_6{}^{2-}$. The completely deprotonated species has the structure

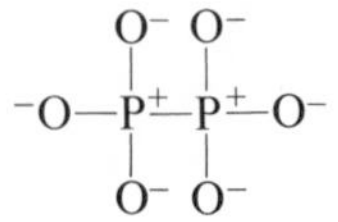

$$\begin{array}{c} \quad O^- \;\; O^- \\ \quad | \quad\; | \\ {}^-O-\overset{+}{P}-\overset{+}{P}-O^- \\ \quad | \quad\; | \\ \quad O^- \;\; O^- \end{array}$$

An isomer of the monoprotonated species has been observed:

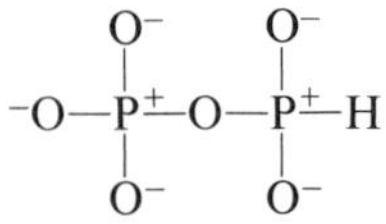

$$\begin{array}{c} \quad O^- \qquad O^- \\ \quad | \qquad\quad | \\ {}^-O-\overset{+}{P}-O-\overset{+}{P}-H \\ \quad | \qquad\quad | \\ \quad O^- \qquad O^- \end{array}$$

8.7 OXIDES AND OXYACIDS OF ARSENIC. **Arsenic(III) oxide** exists in two modifications: arsenolite (mp 278°) and claudetite (mp 312°). Arsenolite consists of a lattice of As_4O_6 molecules similar to P_4O_6 molecules (Fig. 8.2); this is the modification which is formed by condensation of the vapor or by crystallization from solution. Claudetite has a simple layer structure: a hexagonal net of arsenic atoms joined together by oxygen atoms. Arsenic(III) oxide is used in the manufacture of pesticides and weed-killers. The oxide itself is fairly poisonous to humans (fatal dose 0.06–0.2 g), but by starting out with small doses and gradually increasing them, a tolerance can be developed which permits the consumption of gram amounts. As_4O_6 is only slightly soluble in water (0.207 M at 25°), and the rate of solution is very low. The structure of the resulting **arsenious acid** is not established; the formula is usually assumed to be H_3AsO_3. It is clear from the equilibrium constants for the following reactions that, although arsenic(III) oxide is only weakly acidic, it is much more acidic than it is basic:

$$H_3AsO_3 = H^+ + H_2AsO_3{}^- \qquad K = 5.9 \times 10^{-10}$$

$$H_3AsO_3 = AsO^+ + OH^- + H_2O \qquad K = 5 \times 10^{-15}$$

The oxidation potential diagrams for arsenic are given on page 101. It can be seen that, unlike phosphorus and phosphorous acid, neither arsenic nor arsenious acid is unstable with respect to disproportionation. Concentrated nitric acid oxidizes arsenic to **arsenic acid**, H_3AsO_4, which is triprotonic: $K_1 = 5.6 \times 10^{-3}$, $K_2 = 1.7 \times 10^{-7}$, $K_3 = 3 \times 10^{-12}$. By careful dehydration of arsenic acid, **As_2O_5** can be prepared.

Acidic Solutions:

$$AsH_3 \xrightarrow{\;0.38\;} As \xrightarrow{\;-0.25\;} H_3AsO_3 \xrightarrow{\;-0.56\;} H_3AsO_4$$

Basic Solutions:

$$AsH_3 \xrightarrow{\;1.21\;} As \xrightarrow{\;0.68\;} H_2AsO_3^- \xrightarrow{\;0.67\;} AsO_4{}^{3-}$$

Sodium monohydrogen arsenate, Na_2HAsO_4, undergoes thermal dehydration to give a **diarsenate**, $Na_4As_2O_7$, but when this compound is dissolved in water it is completely hydrolyzed to the orthoarsenate. Similarly, dehydration of NaH_2AsO_4 yields a **polyarsenate**, $(NaAsO_3)_x$, which is completely broken down to orthoarsenate in water. When mixtures of NaH_2AsO_4 and NaH_2PO_4 are fused, polyarsenatophosphates, containing a statistical distribution of arsenic and phosphorus atoms, are formed:

$$\begin{array}{ccccccccc}
& O^- && O^- && O^- && O^- && O^- \\
& | && | && | && | && | \\
-P^{\pm}\!-\!O\!-\!As^{\pm}\!-\!O\!-\!P^{\pm}\!-\!O\!-\!P^{\pm}\!-\!O\!-\!As^{\pm}\!-\!O^- \\
& | && | && | && | && | \\
& O^- && O^- && O^- && O^- && O^-
\end{array}$$

Apparently the As—O—P and As—O—As links undergo rapid hydrolytic cleavage, because when these **polyarsenatophosphates** are dissolved in water, only orthoarsenate and a mixture of polyphosphates and orthophosphate are formed. When an equimolar mixture of Na_2HPO_4 and Na_2HAsO_4 is heated, the anion O_3P—O—$AsO_3{}^{4-}$ is formed.

8.8 SULFIDES. At temperatures below about 100°, sulfur and phosphorus do not react, but liquid and solid solutions may be obtained. At temperatures above about 100°, reaction takes place, and the crystalline compounds P_4S_3, P_4S_5, P_4S_7, and P_4S_{10} may be isolated. P_4S_{10}, which unfortunately is often referred to as phosphorus pentasulfide, has practically the same structure as P_4O_{10}, with sulfur atoms replacing the oxygen atoms. The structures of the other phosphorus sulfides are shown in Fig. 8.5. P_4S_3 is used in the manufacture of non-safety matches; the heads of such matches consist of a mixture of P_4S_3, PbO_2, powdered glass, and glue. The friction of striking raises the temperature to the point where the PbO_2 rapidly oxidizes the P_4S_3.

The mineral realgar, **As_4S_4**, has a molecular structure much like that of S_4N_4 (Fig. 6.2), except that the arsenic atoms occupy the positions of the S_4N_4 sulfur atoms, and the sulfur atoms occupy the positions of the S_4N_4 nitrogen atoms. On exposure to light, the compound decomposes to

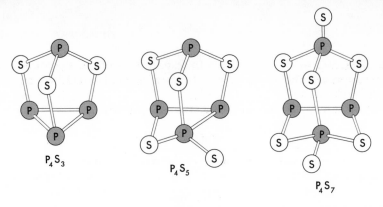

FIGURE 8.5   *Structures of P_4S_3, P_4S_5, and P_4S_7.*

arsenic(III) sulfide, **As_2S_3,** which has a structure analogous to that of claudetite (As_2O_3). Arsenic(III) sulfide can be precipitated by passing H_2S into an acidified solution of arsenious acid; the sulfide is insoluble even in concentrated hydrochloric acid. The acidic character of As_2S_3 is demonstrated by its dissolution in sulfide solutions to form thioarsenite and its dissolution in hydroxide solutions to form arsenite and thioarsenite:

$$As_2S_3 + 3\,S^{2-} \longrightarrow 2\,AsS_3^{3-}$$

$$As_2S_3 + 4\,OH^- \longrightarrow H_2AsO_3^- + AsS_3^{3-} + H_2O$$

Polysulfide solutions oxidize As_2S_3 to **thioarsenate:**

$$As_2S_3 + 2\,S_2^{2-} + S^{2-} \longrightarrow 2\,AsS_4^{3-}$$

In dilute acidic solutions, arsenic acid is slowly reduced by hydrogen sulfide to arsenic(III) sulfide:

$$5\,H_2S + 2\,H_3AsO_4 \longrightarrow As_2S_3 + 8\,H_2O + 2\,S$$

Arsenic(V) sulfide, As_2S_5, may be precipitated from concentrated hydrochloric acid solutions of arsenic(V). The sulfide is unstable with respect to As_2S_3 and sulfur. It is soluble in sulfide solutions, forming thioarsenate:

$$As_2S_5 + 3\,S^{2-} \longrightarrow 2\,AsS_4^{3-}$$

8.9 PHOSPHORUS-NITROGEN COMPOUNDS.   The phosphorus trihalides react with ammonia in cold, inert solvents to form **phosphorus triamide:**

$$PCl_3 + 6\,NH_3 \longrightarrow P(NH_2)_3 + 3\,NH_4Cl$$

Similar treatment of phosphorus pentachloride yields a polymeric amide-imide of empirical composition **PN_3H_4:**

$$PCl_5 + 8\,NH_3 \longrightarrow 5\,NH_4Cl + PN_3H_4$$

Both $P(NH_2)_3$ and PN_3H_4 undergo stepwise pyrolysis to eventually form the polymer $(PN)_x$:

$$P(NH_2)_3 \xrightarrow{-NH_3} P_2(NH)_3 \xrightarrow{-H_2} P_2N_3 \searrow_{N_2}$$
$$(PN)_x$$
$$PN_3H_4 \xrightarrow{-NH_3} PN_2H \xrightarrow{-NH_3} P_3N_5 \nearrow_{N_2}$$

Phosphorus tri-N-methylimide, $P_4[N(CH_3)]_6$, is formed in the reaction of phosphorus trichloride with excess methylamine, CH_3NH_2. This compound probably has a structure analogous to that of P_4O_6, in which the four phosphorus atoms are linked together by $CH_3N{\overset{\frown}{}}$ groups.

Phosphoryl triamide, $PO(NH_2)_3$, is prepared by the reaction of ammonia with phosphoryl chloride in a cold, inert solvent:

$$POCl_3 + 6\,NH_3 \longrightarrow PO(NH_2)_3 + 3\,NH_4Cl$$

The compound undergoes partial hydrolysis in aqueous base to form the **diamidophosphate** ion:

$$
\begin{array}{ccc}
\overset{\displaystyle NH_2}{\underset{\displaystyle NH_2}{^-O-P^{\pm}-NH_2}} + OH^- & \longrightarrow & \overset{\displaystyle NH_2}{\underset{\displaystyle NH_2}{^-O-P^{\pm}-O^-}} + NH_3
\end{array}
$$

The free acid, **diamidophosphoric acid** ($pK \approx 5.0$), may be precipitated by the addition of excess cold acetic acid. **Monoamidophosphoric acid** may be prepared by the formation of diphenyl chlorophosphate followed by its ammonolysis and saponification:

$$POCl_3 \xrightarrow{C_6H_5OH} (C_6H_5O)_2POCl \xrightarrow{NH_3} (C_6H_5O)_2PO(NH_2)$$
$$\downarrow KOH$$
$$(HO)_2PO(NH_2) \xleftarrow[ClO_4^-]{H^+} KHPO_3NH_2$$

Monoamidophosphoric acid is a diprotonic acid with $pK_1 \sim 2.8$ and $pK_2 \sim 8.2$.

When phosphorus pentachloride and ammonium chloride are heated together, a series of cyclic compounds known as the **phosphonitrilic chlorides** are formed:

$$PCl_5 + NH_4Cl \longrightarrow \frac{1}{n}(PNCl_2)_n + 4\,HCl$$

Members of this series with values of n from 3 to 8 have been isolated. The best-known member is the trimer, $P_3N_3Cl_6$ (mp 114°, bp 256.5°), the structure of which is

When the cyclic compounds are heated to approximately 300°, a rubber-like chain **polymer** $(PNCl_2)_n$ is formed. X-ray diffraction studies show that this rubber achieves structural regularities when it is stretched into a fiber, but is amorphous when relaxed. The same behavior is found with natural rubber. The value of n is at least 200. A wide variety of substitution reactions have been carried out with the phosphonitrilic chlorides. For example, the chlorine atoms can be replaced by fluorine atoms or amino groups:

$$P_3N_3Cl_6 + 6\,NaF \xrightarrow{\;C_6H_5NO_2\;} NaCl + P_3N_3F_6$$

$$P_3N_3Cl_6 + 12\,NH_3 \xrightarrow{\;liquid\ NH_3\;} 6\,NH_4Cl + P_3N_3(NH_2)_6$$

Partial substitution gives products which show structural isomerism.

8.10 ANALYSIS.   Phosphorus compounds can be easily converted to **orthophosphate** by hydrolysis or oxidation with nitric acid; the orthophosphate ion may then be detected by treatment with a solution of ammonium molybdate in nitric acid, causing precipitation of yellow **ammonium molybdophosphate:**

$$H_3PO_4 + 12\,MoO_4{}^{2-} + 3\,NH_4{}^+ + 21\,H^+ \longrightarrow (NH_4)_3PMo_{12}O_{40} + 12\,H_2O$$

Arsenate forms a similar precipitate, but only if the solution is boiled. The precipitation of ammonium molybdophosphate may be used as a preliminary separation from interfering elements in the quantitative analysis of phosphorus. The precipitate may either (1) be dissolved in aqueous ammonia and the phosphate reprecipitated as $MgNH_4PO_4$, followed by ignition and weighing as $Mg_2P_2O_7$, or (2) be titrated with standard hydroxide solution:

$$(NH_4)_3PMo_{12}O_{40} + 23\,OH^- \longrightarrow HPO_4{}^{2-} + 12\,MoO_4{}^{2-} + 3\,NH_4{}^+ + 11\,H_2O$$

Hypophosphorous acid may be quantitatively oxidized to phosphorous acid with ceric ion in acid solution:

$$H_3PO_2 + 2\,Ce^{4+} + H_2O \longrightarrow H_3PO_3 + 2\,Ce^{3+} + 2\,H^+$$

The latter reaction is complete in two hours at room temperature. Both

hypophosphorous acid and **phosphorous acid** are oxidized to orthophosphate by boiling with excess ceric solution; the excess ceric ion can be back-titrated with a standard reducing agent to determine the hypophosphorous acid plus phosphorous acid.

Arsenic, in either the $+3$ or $+5$ state, may be detected in solution by treatment with stannous ion in concentrated hydrochloric acid. A black precipitate of elementary arsenic forms. In low concentrations, **arsenious acid** and **arsenic acid** may be quantitatively reduced to **arsine** by the action of active metals in acid solutions:

$$3\,Zn + 6\,H^+ + H_3AsO_3 \longrightarrow AsH_3 + 3\,H_2O + 3\,Zn^{2+}$$

$$4\,Zn + 8\,H^+ + H_3AsO_4 \longrightarrow AsH_3 + 4\,H_2O + 4\,Zn^{2+}$$

Extremely small amounts of arsine may be detected by its thermal decomposition in a glass tube to give a mirror of elementary arsenic:

$$AsH_3 \longrightarrow As + \tfrac{3}{2}H_2$$

or by its reaction with silver nitrate to give a yellow precipitate which turns black because of the formation of metallic silver:

$$AsH_3 + 6\,Ag^+ + 3\,NO_3^- \longrightarrow Ag_3As\cdot 3\,AgNO_3 + 3\,H^+$$

$$Ag_3As\cdot 3\,AgNO_3 + 3\,H_2O \longrightarrow 6\,Ag + 3\,H^+ + 3\,NO_3^- + H_3AsO_3$$

Arsenic may be gravimetrically determined as As_2S_3 or as $Mg_2As_2O_7$.

It is interesting to note that volumetric methods of analysis are based both on the quantitative oxidation of **arsenious acid** by triiodide and on the quantitative reduction of **arsenic acid** by iodide. This apparent paradox is explicable by considering the pH-dependence of the equilibrium reaction

$$H_3AsO_3 + I_3^- + H_2O = H_3AsO_4 + 3\,I^- + 2\,H^+$$

for which

$$K_{25^\circ} = (H^+)^2\,\frac{(I^-)^3(H_3AsO_4)}{(I_3^-)(H_3AsO_3)} = 0.16.$$

At pH 7 ($HCO_3^- - H_2CO_3$ buffer)

$$\frac{(I^-)^3(H_3AsO_4)}{(I_3^-)(H_3AsO_3)} = \frac{0.16}{(10^{-7})^2} = 1.6 \times 10^{13}$$

and consequently arsenious acid can be titrated with triiodide, or *vice-versa*. In 6 M HCl,

$$\frac{(I^-)^3(H_3AsO_4)}{(I_3^-)(H_3AsO_3)} = \frac{0.16}{(6)^2} = 4.5 \times 10^{-3}$$

and consequently arsenic acid is quantitatively reduced by an excess of iodide (the triiodide can be titrated with thiosulfate).

SUGGESTED REFERENCES

Cowley, A. H., "The Structures and Reactions of the Phosphorus Sulfides," *J. Chem. Education,* 41 (1964), 530.

George, J. W., "Halides and Oxyhalides of the Elements of Groups Vb and VIb," *Progress in Inorg. Chem.,* 2, (1960), 33.

Grayson, M. and E. J. Griffith, eds, various volumes of *Topics in Phosphorus Chemistry.* New York: Interscience, 1964.

Thilo, E., "Condensed Phosphates and Arsenates," *Advances in Inorg. Chem. and Radiochem.,* 4, (1962), 1.

Van Wazer, J. R., *Phosphorus and its Compounds.* New York: Interscience, 1958.

9

Antimony

9.1 GENERAL CHEMICAL CHARACTERISTICS.
There are several striking differences
between the chemistry of antimony
and that of phosphorus and arsenic.
For example, in the $+3$ oxidation
state, antimony can exist in aqueous
solution as the cationic species SbO^+,
whereas such a species is unknown for
phosphorus(III) and known only in
strongly acid solutions of arsenic(III).
In the $+5$ oxidation state, antimony
has a marked tendency to acquire a
coordination number of 6. Thus antimony compounds structurally analogous to the phosphates and arsenates
are unknown. Instead of SbO_4 units,
SbO_6 units are found. Even in liquid
antimony pentafluoride, the antimony
has a coordination number of 6, rather
than 5 as in the case of phosphorus in
PF_5 and arsenic in AsF_5. It will be
noted that the unique features of antimony which we have discussed are explicable in terms of its larger size.

Although the cationic tendencies of
$Sb(III)$ suggest metallic behavior,
most of the chemistry of antimony is
characteristic of a non-metal; therefore this chapter is appropriate in this
book.

**9.2 OCCURRENCE, PREPARATION, AND
PROPERTIES.** Antimony is a relatively
rare element (constituting about 1 part
per million of the earth's crust) that is

found principally in the form of **stibnite**, Sb_2S_3, **valentinite**, Sb_2O_3, **senarmontite**, Sb_2O_3, and **kermasite**, $Sb_2O_3 \cdot 2\ Sb_2S_3$. These ores are generally reduced to the element by reduction with carbon, either by treatment with charcoal in an alkaline flux containing sodium sulfate and either sodium hydroxide or potassium hydroxide, or by treatment with coke in a blast furnace. In some cases, the sulfide ores are roasted to the oxide and treated as above; in other cases they are melted and reduced with iron metal.

The principal use of antimony metal is as an alloying ingredient for imparting strength to lead. The most important alloys are type metal and the lead alloy used in storage battery plates.

Antimony melts at 630° and boils at 1640°. It generally exists in a silver-white, brittle, **metallic form** which has the same crystal structure as black phosphorus. When antimony vapor is condensed at very low temperatures, a **yellow form** is obtained which transforms to the metallic form at temperatures above $-90°$. The yellow form probably has an Sb_4 molecular structure, analogous to that of yellow phosphorus.

9.3 ANTIMONIDES AND STIBINE. Various tripositive elements form semiconducting compounds with antimony, such as InSb, GaSb, and AlSb. A small but significant amount of antimony is used in the industrial preparation of these compounds, which find use in various electronic devices. The alkali and alkaline-earth metals form **antimonides** of composition M_3^ISb and $M_3^{II}Sb_2$ which hydrolyze in acidic solutions to give **stibine**, SbH_3. Stibine may also be prepared by the reduction of acidic aqueous solutions of Sb(III) by the hydroborate ion. Stibine is a very poisonous gas (m.p. $-88°$, b.p. $-18.4°$) which decomposes to its elements on heating or on exposure of the gas to antimony metal:

$$SbH_3 \longrightarrow Sb + \tfrac{3}{2} H_2 \qquad \Delta H° = -34.7 \text{ kcal/mole}$$

If a small portion of a sample of pure stibine at a pressure greater than $\tfrac{1}{3}$ atmosphere is heated, as by sparking or application of a torch to the side of the container, a rapid flame passes through the sample, and quantitative decomposition to the elements takes place. This process has been used in the calorimetric determination of the heat of formation of stibine and of mixtures of stibine with other thermally unstable hydrides which, in the absence of stibine, would not quantitatively decompose on sparking.

9.4 HALIDES. All the trihalides of antimony are known; their physical properties are summarized in Table 9.1. These are generally prepared by reaction of the appropriate halogen with excess antimony, but SbF_3 is more easily prepared by halogen exchange between the trichloride and hydrogen fluoride. When antimony trichloride, bromide, and iodide are treated with an excess of water, the slightly soluble oxyhalides, SbOCl, SbOBr, and SbOI are formed. Further hydrolysis yields compounds of composition $Sb_4O_5X_2$.

The trihalides dissolve in solutions of the corresponding hydrohalic acid or alkali metal halide to form complexes of the type SbX_4^-, and probably SbX_5^{2-} and SbX_6^{3-}. Complex salts of compositions $MSbX_4$, M_2SbX_5, M_3SbX_6, and $M_3Sb_2X_9$ have been isolated from such solutions. For chloride solutions, the following equilibrium quotients have been determined:

$$\frac{(SbCl_6^{3-})}{(SbCl_4^-)(Cl^-)^2} = 0.17 \qquad \frac{(SbCl_4^-)}{(SbCl_3)(Cl^-)} = 10$$

The only known pentahalides of antimony are the pentafluoride and pentachloride, whose physical properties are listed in Table 9.1. The pentachloride molecule has a trigonal bipyramid configuration in both the vapor and solid states, but when it is coordinated to a Lewis base, as in $Cl_3PO \cdot SbCl_5$ or $S_4N_4 \cdot SbCl_5$, the antimony atom is octahedrally coordinated, with the chlorine atoms at the corners of a tetragonal pyramid.

The fluorine nuclear magnetic resonance spectrum* of liquid SbF_5 indicates the presence of three structural types of fluorine atoms, in an abundance ratio of $1:2:2$. This result, together with the fact that liquid SbF_5 is extremely viscous and easily supercooled, has been taken as evidence for the chain structure shown in Fig. 9.1. Each antimony atom is hexacoordinate, and is bound to two linking fluorine atoms (type A), two fluorine atoms which are *trans* to linking fluorine atoms (type B), and two fluorine atoms which are *trans* to each other (type C). Note that the type A fluorine atoms are always *cis* to each other.

Complex salts of the types $MSbF_6$ and $MSbCl_6$, in which the antimony is octahedrally coordinated, are known. The pentafluoride forms a dihydrate, which probably has the structure $(H_3O^+)(SbF_5OH^-)$. Violet-black salts of composition M_2SbX_6, apparently containing antimony of oxidation state $+4$, may be crystallized from chloride and bromide solutions containing both Sb(III) and Sb(V). The salts are diamagnetic, ruling out

---

* See *proton* magnetic resonance in Sec. 1.6.

Table 9.1 SOME PROPERTIES OF
THE ANTIMONY HALIDES

Halide	Melting Point (°C)	Boiling Point (°C)
SbF_3	292	319(subl)
SbF_5	8.3	150
$SbCl_3$	73.4	223
$SbCl_5$	5	140
$SbBr_3$	96.6	280
SbI_3	167	401

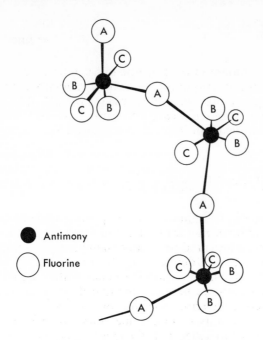

Antimony

Fluorine

FIGURE 9.1 *Schematic chain structure of SbF₅ polymer. From C. J. Hoffman, B. E. Holder, and W. L. Jolly, Journal of the American Chemical Society, 62 (1958), 365. Reprinted by permission of the American Chemical Society.*

the possibility of a simple +4 oxidation state, and have crystal structures like that of $KPtCl_6$. It is believed that the salts contain a regular lattice of $SbCl_6^{3-}$ and $SbCl_6^-$ ions, and that they should be formulated as $M_4(Sb^{III}Cl_6)(Sb^VCl_6)$. The color may be attributed to the mobility of the electrons.

9.5 OXIDES AND OXYACIDS.

Antimony(III) oxide exists in two modifications. **Senarmontite** (the cubic form, stable below 570°) consists of discrete tetrahedral Sb_4O_6 molecules, analogous in structure to P_4O_6. **Valentinite** (the orthorhombic form, stable above 570°) consists of infinite double chains as shown below. This latter modification, although it is unstable at

$$\begin{array}{ccccccc}
& \text{O} & & \text{O} & & \text{O} \\
\diagdown & \diagup \diagdown & & \diagup \diagdown & & \diagup \diagdown \\
& \text{Sb} & & \text{Sb} & & \text{Sb} \\
\text{O} & & \text{O} & & \text{O} \\
& \diagdown & & \diagdown & & \diagdown \\
& \text{Sb} & & \text{Sb} & & \text{Sb} \\
\diagup \diagdown & & \diagup \diagdown & & \diagup \diagdown \\
& \text{O} & & \text{O} & & \text{O}
\end{array}$$

room temperature, is the form which precipitates when base is added to a solution of antimony trichloride in water. This form of antimony(III) oxide is soluble in water only to the extent of 2.9×10^{-5} mole of Sb_2O_3 per liter. The oxide is *amphoteric*—that is, it shows increased solubility in both acid and basic solutions. In solutions of non-complexing acids such as perchloric acid and *dilute* hydrochloric acid, the solubility has been found to be directly proportional to the hydrogen ion concentration. This result indicates that the dissolved species has a single positive charge, and we write:

$$\tfrac{1}{2} Sb_2O_3 + H^+ = SbO^+ + \tfrac{1}{2} H_2O \qquad K_{25°} = 7.7 \times 10^{-4}$$

$$\tfrac{1}{2} Sb_2O_3 + \tfrac{1}{2} H_2O = SbO^+ + OH^- \qquad K_{25°} = 7.7 \times 10^{-18}$$

The SbO^+ ion is called the **antimonyl** ion, but there seems to be no particular reason for formulating it this way rather than as $Sb(OH)_2{}^+$. In solutions of sodium hydroxide, the solubility of Sb_2O_3 is proportional to the hydroxide ion concentration. Hence we write:

$$\tfrac{1}{2} Sb_2O_3 + OH^- = SbO_2^- + \tfrac{1}{2} H_2O \qquad K_{25°} = 8.8 \times 10^{-3}$$

$$\tfrac{1}{2} Sb_2O_3 + \tfrac{1}{2} H_2O = H^+ + SbO_2^- \qquad K_{25°} = 8.8 \times 10^{-17}$$

Antimony(III) forms a very stable complex with the hydrogen tartrate ion:

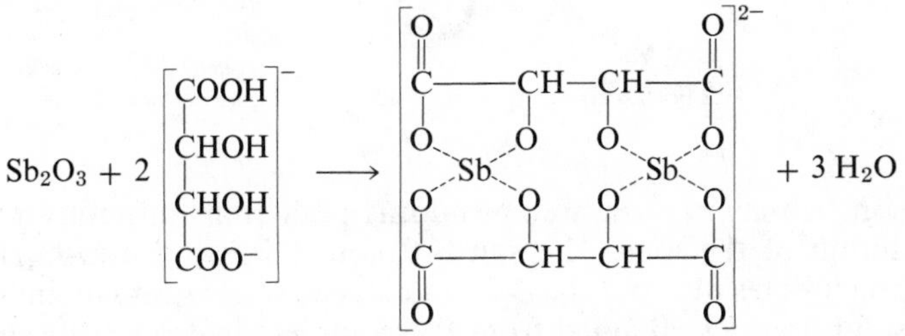

The structure of this complex ion, as formed with natural potassium hydrogen *d*-tartrate*, is shown in Fig. 9.2. Notice that the pictured structure is not superimposable on its mirror image. Consequently, solutions of the ion are *optically active;* that is, they will rotate the plane of polarization of a beam of polarized light passed through them. Potassium antimony *d*-tartrate, $K_2Sb_2(C_4H_2O_6)_2 \cdot 3 H_2O$, is one of the commonest antimony reagents; it finds its principal use in research as a resolving agent for optically active compounds. For example, consider the problem of separating the *d* and *l* optical isomers (mirror image structures) of the *cis*-$Co(en)_2(NO_2)_2{}^+$ ion†, which have the octahedral structures:

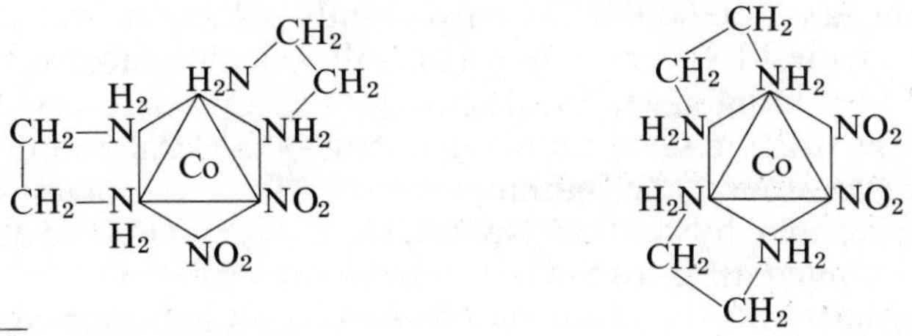

---

* Crystals of this compound form in wine vats.

† en = ethylenediamine, $H_2NCH_2CH_2NH_2$.

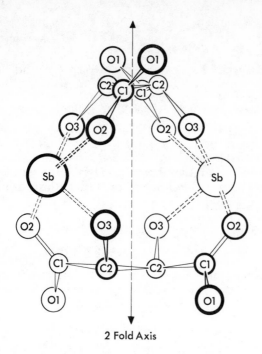

2 Fold Axis

FIGURE 9.2 *The structure of the antimony tartrate ion,* $Sb_2(C_4H_2O_6)_2{}^{2-}$. *The hydrogen atoms are not shown. Figure courtesy of A. Zalkin, D. Templeton, and T. Ueki.*

These isomers may be separated by adding potassium antimony *d*-tartrate to a solution of the ions. The salt $[l\text{-Co(en)}_2(NO_2)_2]_2[Sb_2(d\text{-}C_4H_2O_6)_2]\cdot 2\ H_2O$ precipitates out, and the d-Co $(en)_2(NO_2)_2{}^+$ ions remain in solution.

The solid product obtained from the complete hydrolysis of antimony pentachloride is best formulated as antimony(V) oxide with a variable amount of water of hydration. The hydrated oxide is only sparingly soluble in water, but a metastable solution of **antimonic acid,** $HSb(OH)_6$, as concentrated as 0.02 M can be prepared by passing a potassium antimonate solution through a cation exchange column in the hydrogen form. On standing, polynuclear antimonate species form, and eventually hydrated Sb_2O_5 precipitates. Antimonic oxide dissolves readily in KOH solutions. The monomeric acid is monobasic:

$$HSb(OH)_6 \longrightarrow H^+ + Sb(OH)_6{}^- \qquad K = 2.8 \times 10^{-3}$$

The sodium salt, $NaSb(OH)_6$, is only slightly soluble in water, and has been used as a test for sodium ion. This salt was once incorrectly formulated as a "pyroantimonate," $Na_2H_2Sb_2O_7\cdot 5\ H_2O$. All oxycompounds of Sb(V) whose structures are known have an octahedral coordination of oxygen atoms around the antimony atoms. Thus compounds such as $NaSbO_3$ (prepared by heating $NaSb(OH)_6$), $MgSb_2O_6$, and $Ca_2Sb_2O_7$, consist of infinite lattices of SbO_6 groups sharing oxygen atoms.

When hydrated Sb_2O_5 is heated to about 800°, it is converted, with loss of oxygen, to $Sb_3O_6(OH)$. Further heating at 900° yields the compound SbO_2, which is best regarded as $Sb^{III}Sb^VO_4$.

Acidic Solutions: $\text{SbH}_3 \xrightarrow{\ 0.51\ } \text{Sb} \xrightarrow{\ -0.212\ } \text{SbO}^+ \xrightarrow{\ -0.58\ } \text{Sb}_2\text{O}_5$

Basic Solutions: $\text{SbH}_3 \xrightarrow{\ 1.34\ } \text{Sb} \xrightarrow{\ 0.66\ } \text{SbO}_2^- \xrightarrow{\ 0.4\ } \text{Sb(OH)}_6^-$

The oxidation potential diagrams for antimony are given above. It will be noticed that metallic antimony and Sb(III) are stable with respect to disproportionation. Thus stibine and a solution of antimony trichloride yield a precipitate of the metal, and a potassium antimonate solution is reduced to antimonite by antimony metal. The potential of the antimony-antimony oxide electrode

$$3\,\text{H}_2\text{O} + 2\,\text{Sb} = \text{Sb}_2\text{O}_3 + 6\,\text{H}^+ + 6\,e^- \qquad E° = -0.152$$

rapidly responds to changes in hydrogen ion concentration in the pH range 2 to 8. By casting antimony in air into stick form, it is sufficiently oxidized to serve as an electrode, and it can be used for the potentiometric titration of acids and bases.

9.6 ANALYSIS. The common analytical procedures for antimony are analogous to those for arsenic (see Sec. 8.10.) Antimony may be detected by conversion to stibine, followed by the thermal decomposition of the stibine to antimony and hydrogen or reaction of the stibine with silver nitrate. Antimonite may be quantitatively oxidized to antimonate by titration with iodine in slightly alkaline solution. Antimonic acid may be quantitatively reduced to antimony(III) by excess iodide ion in concentrated hydrochloric acid.

SUGGESTED REFERENCES

George, J. W., "Halides and Oxyhalides of the Elements of Groups Vb and VIb," *Progress in Inorganic Chemistry,* 2 (1960), 33.

Haight, G. P., Jr., and B. Y. Ellis, "Chloride complexes of Sb(III)," *Inorganic Chemistry,* 4 (1965), 249.

Kirschner, S., "Optically Active Coordination Compounds," *Preparative Inorganic Reactions,* 1 (1964), 29. The use of potassium antimony tartrate as a resolving agent.

Wells, A. F., *Structural Inorganic Chemistry.* New York: Oxford University Press, 1962, pp. 662–682.

10

Carbon

10.1 OCCURRENCE. Carbon is one of the most important elements because its atoms form the framework of most of the compounds found in plants and animals. In view of the importance and familiarity of organic compounds, it is somewhat paradoxical that carbon is a relatively minor constituent of the earth's crust ($\sim$0.03 percent), and that it occurs principally in the form of carbonates such as **calcite** and **aragonite** ($CaCO_3$), **magnesite** ($MgCO_3$), and **dolomite** ($CaCO_3 \cdot MgCO_3$). The deposits of coal and petroleum hydrocarbons, which are of biological origin and which are the source of most of our fuel and many of our commercially important chemicals, contain only a small fraction of the earth's carbon.

10.2 ELEMENTARY CARBON. Carbon exists in two crystalline forms, **diamond** and **graphite.** In the diamond crystal, each atom is covalently bonded to four other atoms located at the corners of a regular tetrahedron. Because the energy required to break each C—C bond is fairly high ($\sim$85 kcal/mole), diamond is very difficult to break; it is the hardest substance known. The graphite crystal consists of parallel planes of carbon atoms arranged in a network of hexagonal rings. Here is one of many resonating structures:

114

The planes are loosely held together at a distance of 3.35 Å, whereas the C—C distance in the planes is 1.42 Å. This C—C distance lies between that in the benzene ring (1.39 Å) and that in diamond (1.54 Å), in close agreement with that expected for a bond order of 1.33 (i.e., one-third double-bond character and two-thirds single-bond character). The spaces between the planes of graphite can be occupied by various types of atoms; thus lamellar compounds such as $(CF)_x$, $C_{16}K$, and C_8Br may be formed. Under ordinary conditions, the planes of graphite readily slip over one another, giving the substance lubricant properties. Under high vacuum conditions, this is not true; perhaps the slippage of planes at ordinary pressures is facilitated by a few molecules of nitrogen or oxygen trapped between the layers.

Ever since it was discovered that diamonds and graphite are allotropes of carbon, man has been interested in the conversion of the relatively abundant graphite into the rarer and more valuable diamond. Unfortunately, diamond is thermodynamically unstable with respect to graphite under ordinary conditions ($\Delta F° = 0.692$ kcal/mole at 25°). However, because diamond is more dense than graphite (3.51 *vs.* 2.22 g/cc), diamond becomes the stable modification at high pressures. In recent years, small diamonds have been made by the application of pressures near 100 kilobars to graphite at temperatures near 2500°.

10.3 HYDROCARBONS AND THEIR DERIVATIVES. Carbon has a much greater propensity toward *catenation* (the formation of chains of identical atoms) than any other element. The hydrides of carbon (the hydrocarbons) and their derivatives constitute such a large number of compounds, and they have been studied so extensively, that this branch of chemistry has a special name: organic chemistry. Because organic chemistry is a formidable subject and is covered adequately in other books, we shall say no more about it. The properties of a few hydrocarbons and their derivatives are given in Table 11.2, where they may be compared with those of the analogous silicon and germanium compounds.

10.4 CARBON MONOXIDE. At low temperatures, carbon burns in a deficiency of oxygen to form principally **carbon dioxide**, CO_2; at high temperatures, **carbon monoxide**, CO, is the main product. Approximate values of the equilibrium constant P_{co}^2/P_{co_2} for the reaction:

$$C \text{ (graphite)} + CO_2 = 2\,CO$$

are, at 500°, 0.003; at 600°, 0.07; at 800°, 12. In an excess of oxygen, both carbon and carbon monoxide burn to give carbon dioxide. Carbon monoxide is formed commercially in the high-temperature "water gas" reaction:

$$C + H_2O = CO + H_2$$

In the laboratory, carbon monoxide may be prepared by the action of concentrated sulfuric acid on **formic acid:**

$$HCOOH + H_2SO_4 \longrightarrow CO + H_3O^+ + HSO_4^-$$

The reaction is, in a sense, reversible: carbon monoxide at high pressures reacts with water to form formic acid. Thus carbon monoxide is formic acid anhydride.

The CO molecule is isoelectronic with the N_2 molecule, and these molecules are probably the best examples of the general rule that isoelectronic species have similar physical properties and reactivities. The physical properties may be compared in Table 10.1. Like nitrogen, carbon monoxide is a relatively inert gas at ordinary temperatures; the dissociation energy is extremely high, 256.5 kcal/mole at 25°. The transition **metal carbonyls** have been mentioned in Sec. 2.1.

10.5 CARBON DIOXIDE AND CARBONIC ACID. The combustion of carbon or carbon-containing compounds in excess oxygen yields **carbon dioxide,** CO_2. The oxide is also formed by the pyrolysis of **carbonates** and **bicarbonates:**

$$CaCO_3 \longrightarrow CaO + CO_2$$

$$2\,NaHCO_3 \longrightarrow Na_2CO_3 + H_2O + CO_2$$

Solid carbon dioxide (dry ice) has a vapor pressure of 1 atm at −78.5°; it melts under pressure at −56°. The critical temperature and pressure are 31.35° and 73 atm. The molecule is linear, having the structure O=C=O.

Table 10.1 PHYSICAL PROPERTIES OF CARBON MONOXIDE
AND NITROGEN

	CO	N_2
Melting point, °C	−205.06	−209.97
Boiling point, °C	−191.50	−195.79
Density of liquid	0.793	0.808
Critical temperature, °C	−139	−146.89
Critical pressure, atm	35	33.54
Critical volume, ml	90.1	90.1

The solubility of carbon dioxide in water at 25° at 1 atm pressure is 0.033 M; for convenience it is usually assumed that the dissolved gas exists as **carbonic acid,** H_2CO_3. Making this assumption, the ionization constants at 25° are $K_1 = 4.16 \times 10^{-7}$ and $K_2 = 4.84 \times 10^{-11}$. However, it is known that most of the dissolved carbon dioxide exists as loosely hydrated CO_2, and the true first ionization constant for carbonic acid is about 2×10^{-4}.

The principal equilibrium in an aqueous bicarbonate solution is

$$2\,HCO_3^- = H_2CO_3 + CO_3^{2-} \qquad K_{25°} = 1.16 \times 10^{-4}$$

The reaction may be carried to completion by boiling, which causes the carbonic acid to dissociate to carbon dioxide and water. Of course, the reverse reaction occurs on passing carbon dioxide into carbonate solutions. Even calcium carbonate dissolves to a significant extent in carbonic acid solutions:

$$CaCO_3 + H_2CO_3 \longrightarrow Ca^{2+} + 2\,HCO_3^- \qquad K_{25°} \approx 6 \times 10^{-5}$$

Using the above data and the fact that air contains 0.03 percent by volume of CO_2, the reader may verify that the solubility of limestone in rainwater is about four times that in pure water.

The carbonate ion is isoelectronic with the nitrate ion and, like the latter ion, has a planar structure. The C—O distance, 1.29 Å, is longer than the N—O distance, 1.22 Å, of nitrate.

10.6 HALIDES. The physical properties of the simple tetrahalides of carbon are given in Table 10.2. Many other halides, corresponding to hydrocarbons with the hydrogen atoms partially or completely replaced with halogen atoms, are known. These halides are generally unstable with respect to hydrolysis, but most of them react very slowly with water. **Carbon tetrachloride,** commonly used as a solvent for nonpolar compounds, is prepared by the chlorination of carbon disulfide:

Table 10.2 PROPERTIES OF THE CARBON TETRAHALIDES
AND CARBONYL HALIDES

	Melting Point (°C)	Boiling Point (°C)
CF_4	−183.7	−128.0
CCl_4	−22.9	76.7
CBr_4	90.1	187
CI_4	171	—
COF_2	−114.0	−83.3
$COCl_2$	−127.8	7.6
$CoBr_2$	—	60

$$CS_2 + 3\,Cl_2 \longrightarrow CCl_4 + S_2Cl_2$$

Teflon, a familiar plastic, stable at high temperatures and inert toward most reagents, is prepared by the polymerization of fluoroethylene:

$$xF_2C{=}CF_2 \longrightarrow (-CF_2{-}CF_2-)_x$$

The **carbonyl halides,** COX_2, are planar molecules which react readily with protonic species such as water (to form carbonic acid) and ammonia (to form urea, $CO(NH_2)_2$). The higher reactivity of these halides compared to that of the tetrahalides is probably due to the greater accessibility of the carbon atom to attack by donor atoms such as the oxygen atom of water and the nitrogen atom of ammonia. In tetrahedrally coordinated carbon compounds, the four atoms around each carbon atom are crowded and protect the carbon atom from attack. The physical properties of the carbonyl halides are summarized in Table 10.2.

10.7 CARBON DISULFIDE AND OXYSULFIDE. Carbon disulfide, CS_2, is an obnoxious-smelling, volatile liquid (mp $-111.6°$, bp $46.3°$) which is made by the reaction of sulfur vapor with hot coke. It is used principally as a solvent and for the preparation of carbon tetrachloride. **Carbonyl sulfide,** OCS, is a colorless gas (mp $-138.2°$, bp $-50.2°$) which may be prepared by the high-temperature reaction of CO with sulfur vapor, or by the hydrolysis of thiocyanate in concentrated aqueous acid:

$$SCN^- + 2\,H^+ + H_2O \longrightarrow OCS + NH_4^+$$

Both CS_2 and OCS have linear structures analogous to that of CO_2.

10.8 CARBON-NITROGEN COMPOUNDS. Cyanogen, $(CN)_2$, is a colorless, poisonous gas with the molecular structure $N{\equiv}C{-}C{\equiv}N$. The melting and boiling points are $-27.9°$ and $-21.2°$, respectively. Cyanogen's chemistry resembles that of iodine. Thus cyanogen may be prepared by the oxidation of cyanide by copper(II):

$$2\,Cu^{2+} + 4\,CN^- \longrightarrow 2\,CuCN + (CN)_2$$

and, in alkaline solutions, cyanogen disproportionates to **cyanide** and **cyanate:**

$$(CN)_2 + 2\,OH^- \longrightarrow CN^- + OCN^- + H_2O$$

Sodium cyanide, NaCN, may be prepared by high-temperature reactions involving sodium amide or calcium cyanamide:

$$NaNH_2 + C \longrightarrow H_2 + NaCN$$

$$CaCN_2 + C + Na_2CO_3 \longrightarrow CaCO_3 + 2\,NaCN$$

The cyanide ion, $:C\equiv N:$, is isoelectronic with molecular nitrogen. Like the corresponding iodides, AgCN, $Hg_2(CN)_2$, and $Pb(CN)_2$ are very insoluble. Aqueous solutions of cyanide are alkaline because of extensive hydrolysis to form the weak acid HCN ($K_a = 4 \times 10^{-10}$).

Cyanates are prepared by the action of mild oxidizing agents, such as lead oxide, on cyanides:

$$PbO + KCN \longrightarrow KOCN + Pb$$

Cyanic acid is moderately weak ($K_a = 1.2 \times 10^{-4}$) and decomposes in aqueous solutions to carbonic acid and ammonia.

Thiocyanates are prepared by the reaction of sulfur with fused cyanides:

$$KCN + S \longrightarrow KSCN$$

The aqueous thiocyanate ion is readily oxidized to **thiocyanogen**, $(SCN)_2$:

$$2\,SCN^- = (SCN)_2 + 2\,e^- \qquad E° = -0.77\,v$$

Like the cyanate ion, the thiocyanate ion is linear, with the carbon atom in the middle.

Calcium carbide reacts with nitrogen at about 1,000° to form the calcium salt of cyanamide:

$$CaC_2 + N_2 \longrightarrow CaCN_2 + C$$

Aqueous acid converts calcium cyanamide to **cyanamide**, $H_2N-C\equiv N$, a solid that melts at 46° and is very soluble in water, alcohol, and ether.

10.9 CARBIDES. Carbon and hydrocarbons react at high temperatures with many metals (and in some cases with metal oxides) to form carbides. Saline carbides are formed by the electropositive elements such as the alkali and alkaline-earth metals and the metals of the aluminum family. Carbides of types K_2C_2 and CaC_2 are **acetylides,** and yield acetylene, C_2H_2, upon hydrolysis. Carbides of types Be_2C, Mg_2C, and Al_4C_3 are **methanides,** and yield methane, CH_4, upon hydrolysis. The carbide Mg_2C_3 yields mainly methyl acetylene, $CH_3C\equiv CH$, upon hydrolysis, and is believed to contain C_3^{4-} anions.

A number of transition metals (Ti, Zr, Hf, V, Nb, Ta, Mo, W) form interstitial carbides of composition MC and, in some cases, M_2C. These carbides have extremely high melting points; they are very hard, and they are good electrical conductors.

Various covalent carbides (e.g., CS_2, CCl_4, etc.) have been discussed in this chapter; boron carbide, B_4C, is discussed in Sec. 12.2. The covalent carbide, carborundum, **SiC,** has several crystal structures in which each silicon atom is tetrahedrally bonded to four carbon atoms, and *vice versa.* This extremely hard compound is used as an abrasive, and is made by the reduction of SiO_2 by carbon in an electric furnace.

10.10 ANALYSIS. The carbon content of many substances may be determined by oxidation in a stream of oxygen at high temperatures to CO_2. The CO_2 is usually determined by absorbing it in a tube containing sodium hydroxide and measuring the gain in weight of the tube.

Carbonates and bicarbonates are usually detected by acidification, and reaction of the evolved CO_2 with barium hydroxide solution; a white precipitate of barium carbonate forms. Carbonate and bicarbonate in solution may be quantitatively determined, even when they are present together, by titration with standard acid. The first endpoint, corresponding to the formation of bicarbonate, may be determined using the indicator phenolphthalein or a 6:1 mixture of thymol blue and cresol red. The endpoint corresponding to complete conversion to carbonic acid is determined by using methyl orange indicator.

SUGGESTED REFERENCES

Cotton, F. A. and G. Wilkinson, Ch. 11 ("Carbon") in *Advanced Inorganic Chemistry.* New York: Interscience, 1962.

Hall, H. T., "The Synthesis of Diamond," *J. Chem. Education,* 38 (1961), 484.

Suits, C. G., "Man-Made Diamonds—A Progress Report," *American Scientist,* 52 (1964), 395.

Whitmore, F. C., *Organic Chemistry,* 2nd ed., Vols. 1 and 2. New York: Dover, 1951.

11

Silicon

and Germanium

**11.1 OCCURRENCE AND GENERAL CHAR-
ACTERISTICS.** **Silicon** constitutes about
28 percent of the earth's crust. It
occurs as the dioxide, silica, and in an
enormous variety of silicate minerals.
Thus silicon occupies as prominent a
position in the mineral world as carbon does in the biological world. Although the outer electronic configuration of the silicon atom resembles that
of the carbon atom, the chemistry of
silicon is vastly different from that of
carbon. In fact, there is more resem-
blance between the chemistries of
silicon and boron than between the
chemistries of silicon and carbon. In
our subsequent discussions of indi-
vidual silicon compounds, compari-
sons with the corresponding carbon
compounds will be made. Most of the
differences in structure and properties
can be accounted for by the larger size
of the silicon atom. In almost all its
compounds, silicon has a coordination
number of four; it practically never
has a coordination number less than
four, and occasionally it has a higher
coordination number.

The original Periodic Table, discovered independently by Mendeleev
and Meyer in 1869, had a number of
gaps in it. The gaps were believed to
correspond to undiscovered elements,
and Mendeleev predicted the properties of several of these by interpolation

of the properties of elements adjacent to the gaps in the table. One of these predicted elements was **ekasilicon**—that is, the element lying below silicon in the Periodic Table. In 1886 Winkler, in the course of analyzing a new mineral, discovered a new element which he called **germanium.** After determining some of the physical and chemical properties of germanium, it was clear that germanium corresponded to the ekasilicon of Mendeleev. The predicted properties of ekasilicon may be compared with those of germanium in Table 11.1.

Germanium constitutes only about 10^{-3} percent of the earth's crust and is never found in concentrated deposits. Most of the U.S. supply comes from zinc ores of Oklahoma, Kansas, and Missouri, which contain 0.01–0.1 percent Ge.

The chemistry of germanium is very similar to that of silicon. There are significant differences, however, many of which are in a direction opposite to that which would be extrapolated from the chemistries of carbon and silicon. (For example, Si—X bond energies are greater than either C—X or Ge—X bond energies.) These abnormalities may be due in part to the fact that germanium is only slightly larger than silicon. (The covalent radii are 1.22 and 1.17 Å, respectively.) The rather small increase in size on going from silicon to germanium is a consequence of germanium following, in the Periodic Table, a transition series in which the filling of the d shell is accompanied by a contraction in atomic radius.

11.2 THE ELEMENTS. Silicon is prepared commercially by the reduction of silicon dioxide with carbon or calcium carbide in an electric furnace. Germanium is prepared by reduction of its dioxide with carbon or hydrogen. The exceedingly pure silicon and germanium that are required for use as electronic semiconductors may be prepared by *zone refining.* In this process, a heat source is caused to traverse a rod of the element so that a molten zone moves from one end to the other. Because impurities are more soluble in the melt than in the solid, they are carried toward one end of the rod. The process is repeated several times, and the impure end is removed. In this way, the impurity concentration may be reduced to less than 10^{-9} percent.

Table 11.1 COMPARISON OF THE PROPERTIES
OF EKASILICON AND GERMANIUM

Property	*Ekasilicon*	*Germanium*
Atomic weight	72	72.59
Density	5.5	5.35
Specific heat	0.073	0.076
Density of dioxide	4.7	4.703
Boiling point of tetrachloride	$<100°$	83°
Density of tetrachloride	1.9	1.89
Boiling point of tetraethyl	160°	163.5°
Density of tetraethyl	0.96	0.99

Both silicon and germanium have the same structure as that of diamond. The melting points are 1410° and 937.2°, and the boiling points are 2680° and ~2800°, respectively.

The perfectly pure elements at absolute zero would be electrical insulators, because all the valence electrons would be localized in Si—Si and Ge—Ge bonds. At ordinary temperatures, thermal excitation would free a small fraction of the electrons from the bonds and thus create equal numbers of *conduction electrons* and *holes*. The countercurrent motion of these conduction electrons and holes in an applied electric field, illustrated in Fig. 10.1, corresponds to the intrinsic semiconductivity of the element. By replacing a small fraction of the silicon or germanium atoms with atoms containing more or less than four valence electrons, the conductivity is enormously increased. Replacement by "donor" atoms such as arsenic yields an "*n*-type" semiconductor in which the conductivity is principally due to conduction electrons. (See Fig. 11.2 *A*.) Replacement by "acceptor" atoms such as indium yields a "*p*-type" semiconductor in which the conductivity is principally due to holes. (See Fig. 11.2 *B*.)

The current across a junction between an *n*-type semiconductor and *p*-type semiconductor is as much as 10^6 times greater when the *p*-type semiconductor is made positive relative to the *n*-type semiconductor than when the polarity is reversed. This rectifying characteristic of the *n-p* junction is the basis of the application of silicon and germanium semiconductors in transistors.

11.3 HALIDES. **Silicon tetrafluoride,** SiF_4, is formed when hydrogen fluoride comes in contact with SiO_2 or silicates. (See Sec. 3.5 and Table 3.3.) It is conveniently made by heating a mixture of calcium fluoride and silica with excess concentrated sulfuric acid:

$$2\,CaF_2 + SiO_2 + 4\,H_2SO_4 \longrightarrow 2\,CaSO_4 + SiF_4 + 2\,H_3O^+ + 2\,HSO_4^-$$

The other **silicon tetrahalides** (see Table 4.5) are prepared by the reaction of elementary silicon with the appropriate halogens. When a slow stream of chlorine is passed over calcium silicide at 150°, an homologous series of silicon chlorides is obtained, with approximately the following percentage abundances: 65% $SiCl_4$, 30% Si_2Cl_6, 4% Si_3Cl_8, and 1% Si_4Cl_{10}, Si_5Cl_{12},

FIGURE 11.1 *Conductivity arising from motion of conduction electrons and holes in an applied electric field. Note that holes (or "half-bonds") move when electrons in adjacent bonds move into the holes, leaving new holes behind. The same types of conductivity occur in germanium.*

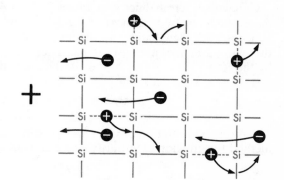

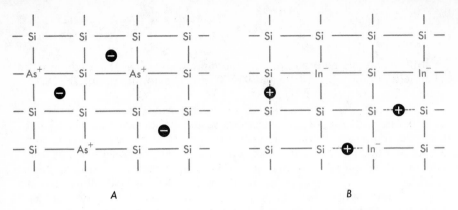

and Si_6Cl_{14}. The other halides of type Si_2X_6 are known, as well as an extensive series of mixed halides such as $SiCl_2I_2$, $SiFCl_3$, and $SiFClBr_2$.

It is instructive to compare the silicon tetrahalides with the carbon tetrahalides as to their reactivity toward basic reagents such as water. Consider carbon tetrachloride and silicon tetrachloride:

$$CCl_4(l) + 2\,H_2O \longrightarrow CO_2 + 4\,H^+ + 4\,Cl^- \qquad \Delta F° = -90.0\ \text{kcal/mole}$$

$$SiCl_4(l) + 2\,H_2O \longrightarrow SiO_2 + 4\,H^+ + 4\,Cl^- \qquad \Delta F° = -66.5\ \text{kcal/mole}$$

Both hydrolyses have tremendous driving forces, the driving force for CCl_4 exceeding that for $SiCl_4$. However, whereas carbon tetrachloride is practically inert toward water at ordinary temperatures, silicon tetrachloride reacts violently with water. The difference in reactivity is partly related to the difference in size of the carbon and silicon atoms. The four chlorine atoms of CCl_4 are sufficiently crowded that they protect the carbon atom from attack, whereas in the case of $SiCl_4$, a water molecule can directly attack the silicon atom with relatively little distortion of the $SiCl_4$ molecule. Also, the silicon atom has empty d orbitals in its valence shell, and these are probably involved in the bonding of the pentacoordinate activated complex, thus reducing the activation energy.

By the controlled hydrolysis of $SiCl_4$, or by its oxidation with O_2, the compound **hexachlorodisiloxane,** $Cl_3Si—O—SiCl_3$, can be prepared.

Germanium tetrahalides (see Tables 3.3 and 4.5) may be prepared from the elements or by treatment of GeO_2 with the appropriate concentrated aqueous hydrogen halide. Germanium differs markedly from silicon in that the $+2$ halides are fairly stable. These saline halides may be prepared by the reversible reaction of the tetrahalide with germanium:

$$GeX_4 + Ge \rightleftharpoons 2\,GeX_2$$

The disproportionation of GeI_2 at approximately $400°$ has been used as a method for growing high-purity single crystals of germanium.

11.4 HYDRIDES AND THEIR DERIVATIVES. All the known hydrides of silicon and germanium are analogous in formula and structure to the alkanes (C_nH_{2n+2}); they are called the **silanes** (Si_nH_{2n+2}) and **germanes** (Ge_nH_{2n+2}). These hydrides were first prepared by the hydrolysis of magnesium silicide and magnesium germanide in aqueous acid, the silanes being approximately distributed as 63% SiH_4, 23% Si_2H_6, 8% Si_3H_8, 4% Si_4H_{10}, and 2% higher hydrides, and the germanes being distributed as 86% GeH_4, 13% Ge_2H_6, and 0.6% Ge_3H_8. Silane, SiH_4, may be more conveniently prepared by the reaction between silicon tetrachloride and lithium aluminum hydride in an ether solvent:

$$SiCl_4 + LiAlH_4 \longrightarrow SiH_4 + AlCl_3 + LiCl$$

Germane, GeH_4, may be conveniently prepared by the reaction of excess acid with an aqueous solution of germanate and hydroborate:

$$GeO_3{}^{2-} + BH_4{}^- + 3\,H^+ \longrightarrow GeH_4 + H_3BO_3$$

The higher silanes (or germanes) may be prepared by the action of a silent electric discharge on silane (or germane).

Unlike the corresponding hydrocarbons, the silanes are very reactive compounds. Except for SiH_4, the silanes inflame spontaneously in air. With weakly alkaline aqueous solutions, the silanes yield hydrogen and silica:

$$Si_2H_6 + 4\,H_2O \longrightarrow 2\,SiO_2 + 7\,H_2$$

With HCl, HBr, and HI, in the presence of aluminum halide catalyst, the hydrogen atoms of silanes may be successively replaced by halogen atoms:

$$SiH_4 + HX \longrightarrow SiH_3X + H_2$$

$$SiH_3X + HX \longrightarrow SiH_2X_2 + H_2$$

$$SiH_2X_2 + HX \longrightarrow SiHX_3 + H_2$$

Reaction of the silanes with free halogens is much more violent and less controllable. The **silyl halides,** SiH_3X, react with water to form the hydrogen halide and **disiloxane,** $H_3Si-O-SiH_3$. The compound SiH_3OH has never been isolated.

Germane is considerably less reactive than silane. Thus, germane is unreactive toward concentrated aqueous alkali. Halogenation reactions proceed analogously to those of the silanes, but the reaction rates are lower.

In Table 11.2, the physical properties of some silicon-hydrogen and germanium-hydrogen compounds are listed with those of the corresponding carbon compounds.

(in all cases the melting point is given first)

$CH_4(-182.5°, -161.5°)$	$SiH_4(-184.7°, -111.4°)$	$GeH_4(-165.9°, -88.36°)$
$C_2H_6(-183.3°, -88.6°)$	$Si_2H_6(-132°, -14.3°)$	$Ge_2H_6(-109°, 30.8°)$
$C_3H_8(-187.7°, -42.1°)$	$Si_3H_8(-117°, 53.0°)$	$Ge_3H_8(-105°, 111.1°)$
$CH_3F(-141.8°, -78.1°)$	$SiH_3F(?, -98.6°)$	$GeH_3F(-22°, 15.6°)$
$CH_3Cl(-97.7°, -24.2°)$	$SiH_3Cl(-118.1°, -30.4°)$	$GeH_3Cl(-52°, 28°)$
$CH_3Br(-93.7°, 3.6°)$	$SiH_3Br(-94°, 1.9°)$	$GeH_3Br(-32°, 52°)$
$CH_3I(-66.5°, 42.4°)$	$SiH_3I(-57.0°, 45.4°)$	$GeH_3I(-15°, 0°/20\ mm)$
$(CH_3)_2O(-141.5°, -24.8°)$	$(SiH_3)_2O(-144°, -15.2°)$	$(GeH_3)_2O(?)$
$(CH_3)_2S(-98.3°, 37.3°)$	$(SiH_3)_2S(-70.0°, 58.8°)$	$(GeH_3)_2S(-34°, 0°/5\ mm)$

11.5 SILICONES. Silicones are the polymeric materials formed by the hydrolysis of alkyl-substituted silicon halides, in which the alkyl groups are usually methyl groups. Four different types of structural units are found in silicones; these are formed by the hydrolyses indicated as follows:

$$(CH_3)_3SiCl \xrightarrow{H_2O} CH_3-\underset{\underset{CH_3}{|}}{\overset{\overset{CH_3}{|}}{Si}}-O- \quad \textit{Terminal group}$$

$$(CH_3)_2SiCl_2 \xrightarrow{H_2O} -O-\underset{\underset{CH_3}{|}}{\overset{\overset{CH_3}{|}}{Si}}-O- \quad \textit{Chain group}$$

$$CH_3SiCl_3 \xrightarrow{H_2O} -O-\underset{\underset{O}{|}}{\overset{\overset{CH_3}{|}}{Si}}-O-$$

$$SiCl_4 \xrightarrow{H_2O} -O-\underset{\underset{O}{|}}{\overset{\overset{O}{|}}{Si}}-O-$$

Branching groups

By hydrolysis of various mixtures of the alkyl-substituted silicon halides, various proportions of the structural units are incorporated in the polymers, and thereby silicones with various physical properties are formed. The silicones may be solids, rubbers, greases, or liquids; they are stable to heat and chemical attack, they have high dielectric strength, and they are water repellent.

11.6 OXIDES. In contrast to molecular carbon dioxide, in which the carbon atom forms double-bonds to two oxygen atoms, silicon dioxide (silica) and germanium dioxide exist as infinite three-dimensional frameworks. In **silica,** each silicon atom forms single-bonds to four oxygen atoms. At ordinary pressures, silica exists in three crystalline forms: quartz (stable up to 870°), tridymite (stable from 870° to 1470°), and cristobalite (stable from 1470° to the melting point, 1710°). These three forms of silica are not readily interconvertible. Each form exists in a low- and high-temperature modification (α and β, respectively) with the transition points 573° for quartz, 120–160° for tridymite, and 200–275° for cristobalite. The conversion of quartz to tridymite involves the breaking of bonds and therefore is a very slow process, whereas the α quartz $\to$ β quartz conversion involves only a small structural distortion, without bond breaking, and consequently is a readily reversible process. Stishovite, a dense, rutile structure of silica in which silicon has a coordination number of six, has been prepared by subjecting silica to 120,000 atm pressure. This same compound has formed under natural conditions in sandstone shattered by meteorite impact.

Molten silica crystallizes slowly, and it usually solidifies to a glass. Glassy silica is used for the construction of certain laboratory glassware, wherewith advantage may be taken of its strength, its low temperature coefficient of expansion (5×10^{-7} deg^{-1}), its transparency to light from 1900 Å to 35,000 Å, or its high softening-point ($\sim 1500°$).

Brown **silicon monoxide,** SiO, is produced by heating Si with SiO_2 at temperatures above 1250°. The monoxide disproportionates on cooling, but it can be obtained as a metastable phase at room temperature by quenching.

Germanium dioxide crystallizes with the rutile structure (in which germanium has a coordination number of six) at low temperatures, and with the α-quartz structure above 1033°. The latter modification is the common one, and, unlike the low-temperature form, is soluble in water (0.0435 M at 25°).

When a solution of germanium dioxide in hydrochloric acid is heated with a strong reducing agent such as hypophosphorous acid, a solution of Ge(II) (in which the germanium exists principally as $GeCl_3^-$ ions) forms. Upon addition of alkali to this solution, yellow hydrous **germanium monoxide** (or "germanous hydroxide") is precipitated. Brown-black anhydrous GeO may be prepared by thermal dehydration of this material or by vacuum sublimation from a mixture of germanium and germanium dioxide. The monoxide is unstable with respect to disproportionation into the metal and dioxide.

11.7 SILICATES. In all ordinary silicates, the silicon atoms are tetrahedrally surrounded by oxygen atoms.* The simplest silicates are the **orthosilicates,** which contain discrete SiO_4^{4-} anions. Examples of this type are olivine, $9\,Mg_2SiO_4 \cdot Fe_2SiO_4$, phenacite, Be_2SiO_4, and grossular,

---

*It is believed that the lower mantle of the earth, where the pressure reaches 1 million atm, contains silicates with hexacoordinate silicon atoms.

$Ca_3Al_2(SiO_4)_3$. In other silicates, the SiO_4 tetrahedra are linked together by the sharing of corners (never by the sharing of edges or faces). Silicates may be classified in terms of the number of oxygen atoms which are shared by each SiO_4 group. The sharing of one oxygen atom corresponds to the **disilicate ion,** O_3Si—O—SiO_3^{6-}, which is found in the rare mineral thortveitite, $Sc_2Si_2O_7$.

The sharing of two oxygen atoms per SiO_4 group corresponds to the so-called **metasilicates** that contain anions of composition $(SiO_3)_n^{2n-}$. These anions can have either a cyclic structure or an infinite chain struc-

ture, formed by the linking of $-\overset{\displaystyle O^-}{\underset{\displaystyle O^-}{\overset{|}{\underset{|}{Si}}}}-O-$ groups. The six-membered ring,

$Si_3O_9^{6-}$, is found in benitoite, $BaTiSi_3O_9$. The infinite chain anion is found in the **pyroxenes,** of which spodumene, $LiAl(SiO_3)_2$, is an example. The **amphiboles** (e.g., tremolite, $Ca_2(OH)_2Mg_5(Si_4O_{11})_2$, and various types of asbestos) contain the "double chain" anion of composition $(Si_4O_{11})_n^{6n-}$ which is pictured in Fig. 11.3. It will be noted that in the amphibole chains one half of the SiO_4 groups share two oxygen atoms, and the other half share three oxygen atoms.

When all the SiO_4 tetrahedra share three corners with other tetrahedra, layer structures are formed which may be considered to be two-dimensional extensions of the network shown in Fig. 11.3. **Talc,** $Mg_3(OH)_2Si_4O_{10}$, and the mica **phlogopite,** $KMg_3(OH)_2Si_3AlO_{10}$ (in which one-quarter of the silicon atoms have been replaced by aluminum atoms), are examples of this type of silicate. As might be expected, these minerals are readily cleaved into sheets.

When the SiO_4 groups share all four corners with other groups, we have the framework structure of silica, SiO_2. If some of the silicon atoms are replaced by aluminum atoms, it is necessary to introduce cations into the structure to neutralize the negative charge of the $(Si, Al)O_2$ framework. The **feldspars** (e.g., orthoclase, $KAlSi_3O_8$) and **zeolites** (e.g., analcite, $NaAlSi_2O_6 \cdot H_2O$) are examples of this type of framework silicate.

When sodium carbonate is fused with silica, and the product is extracted with water, syrupy solutions of **"sodium silicate"** or **"water glass,"** having Na/Si ratios from 0.5 to 4, are obtained. The solutions contain a series of

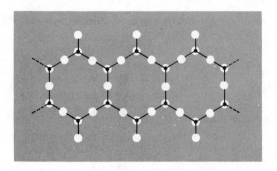

FIGURE 11.3 *An amphibole chain.*

silicate anions such as SiO_4^{4-}, $Si_2O_7^{6-}$, $Si_3O_{10}^{8-}$, $(SiO_3)_4^{8-}$, and higher polysilicate anions. Addition of a sodium silicate solution to excess of dilute aqueous acid yields a solution which probably contains various silicic acids; on standing, the solution turns to a gel of hydrated silica.

11.8 GERMANATES. Many of the oxygen compounds of germanium (e.g., $BeGeO_4$, Zn_2GeO_4, $Sc_2Ge_2O_7$, and $BaTiGe_3O_9$) are isostructural with the corresponding silicates. In these compounds germanium is bonded tetrahedrally to four oxygen atoms. However, it has been observed that germanate analogs of the pyroxenes (see Sec. 11.7) are converted under high pressure to a structure in which the germanium has sixfold coordination.

It is not known whether the species which forms when GeO_2 dissolves in water is H_4GeO_4 or H_2GeO_3. In any event, it is a weak dibasic acid, with $K_1 = 2.6 \times 10^{-9}$ and $K_2 = 2 \times 10^{-13}$. Germanium dioxide dissolves to the extent of $\sim 6\ M$ in $15\ M$ KOH; it is believed that such concentrated solutions contain appreciable amounts of a dimeric species, e.g., $Ge_2O_5^{2-}$.

11.9 ANALYSIS. Silicon compounds are readily converted to silica, which can be identified by the conversion to, and hydrolysis of, SiF_4, as described in Sec. 3.6. Gravimetric methods for silicon are usually based on conversion to silica. Thus silicates are digested with concentrated hydrochloric acid to convert the silicon to silica. (Some silicates require a preliminary fusion with sodium carbonate.) If the silica is contaminated with other oxides (e.g., Al_2O_3 and Fe_2O_3), it may be quantitatively volatilized as SiF_4 by heating with hydrofluoric acid, and the silica determined as the loss in weight after a second ignition.

Germanium is generally determined gravimetrically, by precipitating as the disulfide, GeS_2, and igniting to the dioxide.

SUGGESTED REFERENCES

Ebsworth, E. A. V., *Volatile Silicon Compounds.* Oxford: Pergamon, 1963.
Hannay, N. B., ed., *Semiconductors.* New York: Reinhold, 1959.
MacDiarmid, A. G., "Halogen and Halogenoid Derivatives of the Silanes," *Preparative Inorganic Reactions,* W. L. Jolly, ed. New York: Interscience, 1964, p. 165.
MacDiarmid, A. G., "Silanes and their Derivatives," *Advances in Inorg. Chem. and Radiochem.,* 3, (1961), 207.
Rijkens, F. and G. J. M. Van der Kerk, *Investigations in the Field of Organogermanium Chemistry.* Utrecht: Schotanus and Jens, 1964.
Rochow, E. G., *An Introduction to the Chemistry of the Silicones,* 2nd ed. New York: Wiley, 1951.
Stone, F. G. A., *Hydrogen Compounds of the Group IV Elements.* Englewood Cliffs, N.J.: Prentice-Hall, 1962.
Wells, A. F., *Structural Inorganic Chemistry,* London: Oxford University Press, 1962, Ch. XXI ("Silicon"), pp. 765–816.

12

Boron

12.1 OCCURRENCE. Boron constitutes about 3×10^{-4} percent of the earth's crust; it occurs principally as borates in the barren wastes of south-central and southwest Asia, in portions of Asia Minor, in the pampas of South America, and in the desert areas of the southwestern United States. All these areas are near regions of former intensive volcanic activity. The two principal sources of borates in the United States are (1) an enormous deposit of **borax,** $Na_2B_4O_7 \cdot 10\ H_2O$, and **kernite,** $Na_2B_4O_7 \cdot 4\ H_2O$, lying about 350 feet beneath the Mohave Desert at Boron, California, and (2) an underground lake of brine at Trona, California, known as Searles Lake.

12.2 ELEMENTARY BORON AND BORIDES. Amorphous boron may be prepared by the reduction of boric oxide, B_2O_3, with an electropositive metal such as magnesium. When magnesium is used, the product is usually contaminated with the boride, MgB_2; this species may be minimized by using an excess of boric oxide, but then the product contains boron suboxide in solid solution. Reduction by aluminum yields AlB_{12} and AlB_{10}, and for many years these crystalline borides were thought to be boron. High-purity boron can be prepared by the pyrolysis of diborane, B_2H_6, boron tribro-

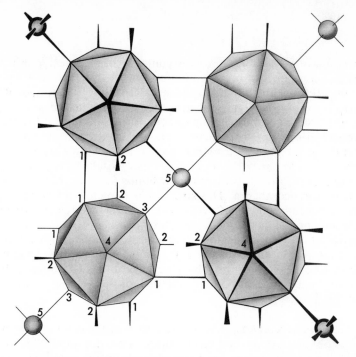

FIGURE 12.1 *Structure of tetragonal boron as viewed in the direction of the c axis. One unit cell is shown. Numbers identify the various structurally nonequivalent boron atoms. All of the extra-icosahedral bonds are shown with the exception of B_4—B_4, which is formed parallel to the c axis from each icosahedron to the icosahedra in cells directly above and below. From L. Pauling,* The Nature of the Chemical Bond, *3rd ed., Fig. 10-1 (Ithaca: Cornell University Press, 1960), p. 364. Copyright 1960 by Cornell University. Used by permission of Cornell University Press.*

mide, BBr_3, or boron triiodide, BI_3, at temperatures near 1000°. The reduction of boron tribromide by hydrogen at a hot metal filament also yields crystalline boron of better than 99 percent purity.

Crystalline boron is a relatively unreactive material. From the oxidation potential:

$$B + 3\,H_2O = H_3BO_3 + 3\,H^+ + 3\,e^- \qquad E° = 0.87$$

one might expect the element to dissolve readily in acid. However, it is unaffected by boiling hydrochloric and hydrofluoric acids and is only slowly dissolved by hot, concentrated nitric acid. The extreme slowness of the reactions with aqueous reagents is probably due to the high activation energy required to break the bonds in the solid. In this respect boron somewhat resembles silicon and germanium. Boron reacts with fluorine at room temperature, and with oxygen and the halogens at elevated temperatures. Some of the important physical properties of boron are: melting point, 2030°; boiling point, 3930°; density, 2.4 g/cc; hardness, 9.3 (diamond = 10); and heat of sublimation at 25°, 135 ±4 kcal/mole.

There are three important modifications of crystalline boron: tetragonal-I, α-rhombohedral and β-rhombohedral. The structures of the first two forms are of interest because they contain icosahedral B_{12} units which are found in a number of boron compounds. (An icosahedron is a polyhedron having 20 faces and 12 corners.) The unit cell of the tetragonal-I form of boron contains four B_{12} icosahedra and two "tetrahedral" atoms, all linked together into a continuous framework, as shown in Fig. 12.1. The α-rhombohedral form consists of a cubic, close-packed arrangement of B_{12} icosahedra; half of the boron atoms of each icosahedron are joined by B—B single bonds to one boron atom of another icosahedron, and the remaining boron atoms form BBB three-center bonds (see Sec. 12.5) to boron atoms of two other icosahedra. This structure is depicted in Fig. 12.2. The structure of boron carbide, B_4C, is similar to the structures of tetragonal-I and α-rhombohedral boron. The structure consists of B_{12} icosahedra which are linked at some corners to other icosahedra and at other corners to the terminal carbon atoms of linear C_3 chains. The nature of the bonding in the various B_{12} icosahedra which we have discussed above is the same as that in the icosahedral boron framework of the $B_{12}H_{12}{}^{2-}$ ion, discussed in Sec. 12.5.

12.3 BORON HYDRIDES. Around the turn of the century, various investigators observed that when metal borides were decomposed by acids, there were formed hydrogen and various obnoxious-smelling gases which burned spontaneously in air with a green flame and which yielded boron when heated. These gases undoubtedly contained mixtures of the boron and silicon hydrides—the silicon hydrides arising from silicon impurity in the borides. It was not until about 1912, at which time Alfred Stock in Germany had developed vacuum-line techniques for handling small amounts of volatile, air-reactive materials, that these gaseous products

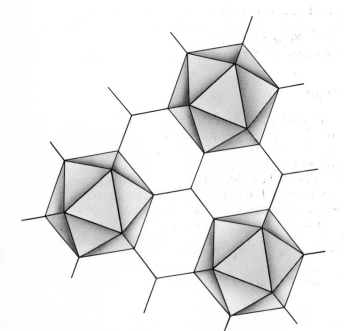

FIGURE 12.2 *Structure of α-rhombohedral boron, showing three B_{12} icosahedra laterally connected by BBB bonds.*

could be separated and characterized. During the following 20 years or so Stock and his coworkers, starting with the volatile hydrolysis products of magnesium boride, isolated and studied the physical and chemical properties of B_2H_6, B_4H_{10}, B_5H_9, B_5H_{11}, B_6H_{10}, and $B_{10}H_{14}$. Further progress in this field was rather slow until, during World War II, Schlesinger and his coworkers at the University of Chicago developed easy methods for the preparation of **sodium hydroborate,** $NaBH_4$—a reagent very useful for the preparation of **diborane,** B_2H_6. Since then, the number of boron hydrides which have been characterized has approximately doubled, the structures of most of the boron hydrides have been determined, and many boron hydride derivatives have been prepared. Some physical properties of the known boron hydrides are presented in Table 12.1.

In the following paragraphs, we shall briefly outline the methods of preparation and a few of the chemical reactions of the boron hydrides and the hydroborate ions. Lack of space prohibits a discussion of each reaction from the point of view of structure and possible mechanism. However, in Sec. 12.5, we shall discuss the structures and bonding in a few of these compounds and shall describe some of the substitution reactions of $B_{10}H_{14}$.

Diborane may be prepared by the reaction of boron trifluoride with sodium hydroborate in an ether solvent such as the dimethyl ether of diethylene glycol (diglyme)

$$3\,NaBH_4 + BF_3 \xrightarrow{\text{diglyme}} 2\,B_2H_6 + 3\,NaF$$

by the reaction of sodium hydroborate with an anhydrous acid such as sulfuric acid or phosphoric acid

Table 12.1 SOME PHYSICAL PROPERTIES
OF THE BORON HYDRIDES

	$mp, °C$	$bp, °C$	$\Delta H_f^\circ (25°, kcal/mole)$ for gases
B_2H_6	-164.86	-92.84	7.5
B_4H_{10}	-120.8	16.1	13.8
B_5H_9	-46.75	58.4	15.0
B_5H_{11}	-123.2	65	22.2
B_6H_{10}	-63.2	108	19.6
B_6H_{12}	-83	80–90	—
B_8H_{12}	~ -20	—	—
B_8H_{18}	—	—	—
B_9H_{15}	2.6	0.8 mm at 28°	—
$B_{10}H_{14}$	99.5	$ca.213$	2.8
$B_{10}H_{16}$	—	—	—
$B_{18}H_{22}$	178.5	—	—
iso-$B_{18}H_{22}$	—	—	—
$B_{20}H_{16}$	199	—	—

$$2\,NaBH_4 + 2\,H_2SO_4 \longrightarrow 2\,Na^+ + 2\,HSO_4^- + B_2H_6 + 2\,H_2$$

and by the reaction of boric oxide with aluminum and hydrogen at high pressure in the presence of aluminum trichloride

$$B_2O_3 + 2\,Al + 3\,H_2 \xrightarrow{AlCl_3} B_2H_6 + Al_2O_3$$

Diborane is extremely poisonous. It reacts quantitatively with water to form boric acid and hydrogen:

$$B_2H_6 + 6\,H_2O \longrightarrow 6\,H_2 + 2\,H_3BO_3$$

Tertiary amines react with diborane to form base-borane adducts:

$$B_2H_6 + 2\,NR_3 \longrightarrow 2\,R_3N:BH_3$$

Ammonia reacts under certain conditions to form a hydroborate containing the $BH_2(NH_3)_2{}^+$ cation:

$$B_2H_6 + 2\,NH_3 \longrightarrow [BH_2(NH_3)_2]BH_4$$

Other salts containing cations of the type $H_2B(base)_2{}^+$ can be prepared by the reaction at elevated temperatures of base-borane adducts, base:BH_3, with onium salts, (base H)$^+X^-$:

$$(CH_3)_3N:BH_3 + [(CH_3)_3NH]I \longrightarrow H_2B[N(CH_3)_3]_2I + H_2$$

B_4H_{10}, B_5H_9, B_5H_{11}, B_6H_{10}, and $B_{10}H_{14}$ have been prepared by the thermal decomposition of diborane. It has been suggested that the thermal decomposition proceeds through the following initial steps:

$$B_2H_6 \rightleftharpoons 2\,BH_3$$

$$B_2H_6 + BH_3 \rightleftharpoons B_3H_9$$

$$B_3H_9 \xrightarrow{slow} B_3H_7 + H_2$$

The rate of disappearance of diborane is found to be proportional to the pressure of diborane raised to the $\frac{3}{2}$ power, a result consistent with this reaction mechanism. However, a chain reaction mechanism involving the species BH_2 and B_2H_5 is also consistent with the data. Much more work will be required to settle this question. These same hydrides, as well as small amounts of B_9H_{15}, can also be prepared by the passage of B_2H_6 through an electric discharge. Small yields of B_8H_{12} are obtained in an electric discharge of a mixture of B_2H_6, B_5H_9, and hydrogen.

In the presence of Lewis bases such as ethers and amines, B_5H_{11} disproportionates to give B_6H_{10} and diborane. The intermediate B_4H_8 is probably involved:

$$2 B_5H_{11} + 4 \text{ base} \longrightarrow 2 \text{ base}:B_4H_8 + 2 \text{ base}:BH_3$$

$$2 \text{ base}:B_4H_8 \longrightarrow B_6H_{10} + 2 \text{ base}:BH_3$$

$$4 \text{ base}:BH_3 \longrightarrow 4 \text{ base} + 2 B_2H_6$$

When hexamethylenetetramine, $(CH_2)_6N_4$, is used as the base, fair yields of B_9H_{15} are obtained. B_5H_{11} may be practically quantitatively converted to tetraborane by treatment with water at $0°$:

$$B_5H_{11} + 3 H_2O \longrightarrow 2 H_2 + H_3BO_3 + B_4H_{10}$$

Inasmuch as B_5H_{11} may be efficiently prepared by the pyrolysis of diborane, this hydrolysis serves as an important preparative method for tetraborane. B_6H_{12} and traces of B_8H_{18} have been prepared by the reaction of the $B_3H_8^-$ ion (see Sec. 12.4) with polyphosphoric acid. Like B_5H_{11}, B_6H_{12} is nearly quantitatively hydrolyzed by cold water to tetraborane:

$$B_6H_{12} + 6 H_2O \longrightarrow B_4H_{10} + 2 H_3BO_3 + 4 H_2$$

When B_5H_9 and hydrogen are passed through an electric discharge, $B_{10}H_{16}$ is formed. Two isomeric forms of $B_{18}H_{22}$ are formed when the $B_{20}H_{18}^{2-}$ ion (Sec. 12.4) is treated with aqueous acid.

12.4 HYDROBORATES (BOROHYDRIDES). Sodium hydroborate,* $NaBH_4$, may be prepared by the reaction of sodium hydride with methyl borate at elevated temperatures:

$$4 NaH + B(OCH_3)_3 \longrightarrow NaBH_4 + 3 NaOCH_3$$

Aqueous solutions of sodium hydroborate are kinetically fairly stable when the pH is high; however, acidic solutions decompose rapidly to hydrogen and boric acid:

$$BH_4^- + H^+ + 3 H_2O \longrightarrow 4 H_2 + H_3BO_3$$

Sodium hydroborate is commonly used as a strong reducing agent in both inorganic and organic syntheses. Two typical reactions are:

$$3 BH_4^- + 4 HSnO_2^- + 7 H^+ + H_2O \longrightarrow 4 SnH_4 + 3 H_3BO_3$$

$$4 \quad \begin{array}{c} R \\ \diagdown \\ C{=}O \\ \diagup \\ R \end{array} + BH_4^- + 4 H_2O \longrightarrow 4 \quad \begin{array}{c} R \\ \diagdown \\ CHOH \\ \diagup \\ R \end{array} + B(OH)_4^-$$

When a solution of sodium hydroborate in the dimethyl ether of triethylene glycol is electrolyzed using a mercury cathode, approximately

---

* Sometimes called sodium tetrahydroborate or sodium borohydride.

half the "theoretical" current is passed before diborane is evolved, and then diborane is evolved at twice the "theoretical" rate. By "theoretical" we mean according to the following half-reaction:

$$BH_4^- = \tfrac{1}{2} B_2H_6 + \tfrac{1}{2} H_2 + e^-$$

The data are explained by assuming the initial formation of the **heptahydrodiborate ion, $B_2H_7^-$:**

$$2\,BH_4^- = B_2H_7^- + \tfrac{1}{2} H_2 + e^-$$

After this reaction has been carried essentially to completion, further passage of current causes the following reaction to take place:

$$B_2H_7^- = B_2H_6 + \tfrac{1}{2} H_2 + e^-$$

Further evidence for the $B_2H_7^-$ ion is found in the fact that the apparent molar solubility of diborane in polyether borohydride solutions (extrapolated to zero pressure of B_2H_6 in order to avoid the effect of the solubility of B_2H_6 in the solvent alone) is one-half the molarity of the borohydride ion.

When ether solutions of sodium borohydride are heated at 100° with diborane, the **octahydrotriborate ion, $B_3H_8^-$,** is formed:

$$B_2H_6 + NaBH_4 \longrightarrow NaB_3H_8 + H_2$$

By suitable variation of the reaction time, the temperature, the diborane pressure, and the solvent, these same reagents can be made to yield the ions **$B_6H_6^{2-}$, $B_{10}H_{10}^{2-}$, $B_{11}H_{14}^-$,** and **$B_{12}H_{12}^{2-}$.** These ions are remarkably resistant toward hydrolysis, and their boron skeletons remain intact throughout a wide variety of reactions in which the hydrogen atoms are replaced by other groups. The boron skeleton of the highly symmetric $B_{12}H_{12}^{2-}$ ion is a regular icosahedron, similar to the B_{12} icosahedra pictured in Figs. 12.1 and 12.2. The bonding in this ion is discussed in Sec. 12.5.

In ethanol-water solutions, decaborane may be titrated with base as a strong monoprotic acid:

$$OH^- + B_{10}H_{14} \longrightarrow H_2O + B_{10}H_{13}^-$$

The anion undergoes an irreversible degradation, but, with care, most of the decarborane may be recovered from the solution after reacidification of the solution. When neutral donor molecules such as $CH_3-C\equiv N:$, $R_3N:$, and $R_3P:$ are heated with decaborane, two of the hydrogen atoms of the decaborane are displaced by the donor molecules:

$$B_{10}H_{14} + 2\,X \longrightarrow B_{10}H_{12}X_2 + H_2$$

When substitution products of this type are heated with bases, the $B_{10}H_{10}^{2-}$ ion is formed:

$$B_{10}H_{12}X_2 + 2\,R_3N \longrightarrow B_{10}H_{10}^{2-} + 2\,R_3NH^+ + 2\,X$$

This ion may be oxidized with aqueous acidified ferric ion to produce the **$B_{20}H_{18}^{2-}$** ion.

12.5 STRUCTURES AND BONDING OF BORON-HYDROGEN COMPOUNDS. The structures and bonding of the boron hydrides and hydroborates may be explained in terms of simple valence theory if we allow the concept of the "three-center bond." The usual covalent bond is a two-center bond; two atoms are held together by a pair of electrons in a molecular orbital formed by the overlap of two atomic orbitals. In a three-center bond, three atoms are held together by a pair of electrons in a molecular orbital formed by the overlap of three atomic orbitals. The two types of three-center bonds which we find in the boron hydrides and their derivatives are the BHB

bond, represented by $B \overset{H}{\diagup\diagdown} B$, and the BBB bond, usually represented

by $B \overset{B}{\diagup\diagdown} B$. In order to satisfactorily explain the bonding in any boron hydride or hydroborate, the following criteria must be fulfilled: (1) The number of valence electrons of all the atoms must equal twice the number of bonds, including both two- and three-center bonds. (2) Each boron atom must contribute four orbitals to the bonding system and must have a complete octet of electrons. (3) The bonding must be consistent with the observed structure of the molecule and with an approximately tetrahedral disposition of orbitals from each boron atom. We shall here describe the structure and bonding of several boron-hydrogen compounds in order to illustrate the application of the three-center bond concept.

First let us consider the **hydroborate ion, BH_4^-.** It is convenient to start the discussion with this species because it involves no three-center bonds. The four hydrogen atoms are tetrahedrally arranged around the central boron atom. The number of valence electrons is eight (three from the boron, one from each hydrogen, and one for the negative charge). If we form a two-center B—H bond between the boron atom and each hydrogen atom by using sp^3 hybrid orbitals of the boron, we shall use all the valence electrons, satisfy the octet rule, and have an ion of the correct geometry. It will be noted that the BH_4^- ion is isoelectronic with methane and the ammonium ion.

Next, consider **diborane, B_2H_6.** This molecule is shaped somewhat like ethylene, CH_2CH_2, with the four terminal hydrogen atoms in the same plane with the two boron atoms. The two bridging hydrogen atoms lie in a plane perpendicular to that of the other atoms:

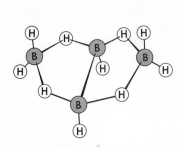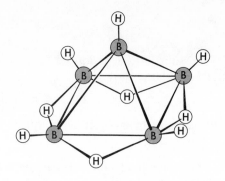

This structure is the result of forming normal B—H bonds to the terminal hydrogen atoms and of forming a pair of BHB bonds between the boron atoms. Notice that the number of valence electrons equals twice the number of bonds, that the boron octets are complete, and that the structure is consistent with the use of tetrahedrally directed sp^3 hybrid orbitals of boron.

Next we shall consider **tetraborane**, B_4H_{10}. The structure of this molecule is indicated in Fig. 12.3, and the bonding may be represented by:

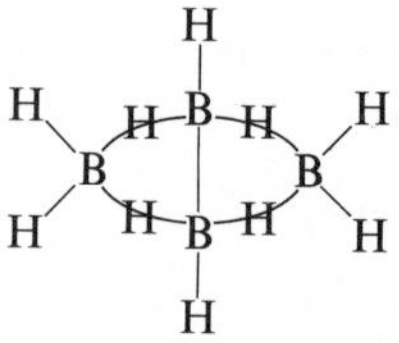

$$
\begin{array}{ccccc}
 & & \text{H} & & \\
 & & | & & \\
\text{H} & \text{H--B--H} & & \text{H} \\
\diagdown & \text{B} & & \text{B} & \diagup \\
\text{H} & \text{H--B--H} & & \text{H} \\
 & & | & & \\
 & & \text{H} & &
\end{array}
$$

It will be noted that there are six B—H bonds, four BHB bonds, and one B—B bond in the molecule. The reader can verify that our three bonding criteria are fulfilled.

The structure of **pentaborane-9**, B_5H_9, is given in Fig. 12.3. One representation of the bonding is as follows:

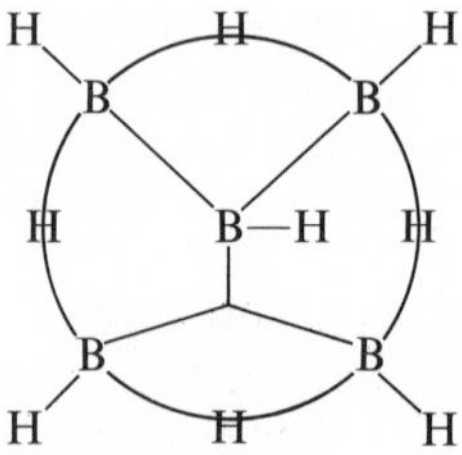

$$
\begin{array}{ccccc}
\text{H} & & \text{H} & & \text{H} \\
\diagdown & \text{B} & & \text{B} & \diagup \\
\\
\text{H} & & \text{B--H} & & \text{H} \\
\\
 & \text{B} & & \text{B} & \\
\diagup & & & & \diagdown \\
\text{H} & & \text{H} & & \text{H}
\end{array}
$$

The actual molecule may be considered a resonance hybrid of the four structures of this type which may be observed by successively rotating this page by 90°. It can be seen that the 24 valence electrons occupy 12 bonds: there are five B—H bonds, four BHB bonds, two B—B bonds and one BBB bond. Here we have our first example containing all the types of bonds found in the boron hydrides.

Now let us consider the interesting ion $B_{12}H_{12}{}^{2-}$. In this species, the boron atoms are arranged at the corners of a regular icosahedron with a hydrogen atom attached to each boron atom. Thus, the ion has a cage structure. The boron framework may be considered to be a resonance hybrid of many conceivable structures having three B—B bonds and ten BBB bonds. One possible arrangement of these bonds is pictured in Fig. 12.4.

Finally we shall discuss **decaborane,** $B_{10}H_{14}$. The basket-like structure of this hydride is shown in Fig. 12.5. The molecule may be likened to a $B_{12}H_{12}{}^{2-}$ ion from which two adjacent BH groups have been removed and which has then been patched up by the addition of two protons and two hydrogen atoms to form four BHB bonds. As in the cases of B_5H_9 and $B_{12}H_{12}{}^{2-}$, the molecule is a resonance hybrid. One distribution of bonds in the boron skeleton is shown in Fig. 12.6, where the boron skeleton has been flattened out to aid in showing all the bonds.

An intriguing unsolved problem in the chemistry of decaborane is that of predicting the positions of substitution when hydrogen atoms of decaborane are replaced by other groups. For example, substitution by alkyl groups can be accomplished in two ways: by reaction with alkyl bromides in the presence of aluminum chloride catalyst

$$RBr + B_{10}H_{14} \xrightarrow{AlCl_3} B_{10}H_{13}R + HBr$$

or by reaction with lithium alkyls

$$LiR + B_{10}H_{14} \longrightarrow LiH + B_{10}H_{13}R$$

Reactions of the first type yield products with the alkyl groups in only

FIGURE 12.4 *Front and back sides of the boron framework of the* $B_{12}H_{12}{}^{2-}$ *ion. The particular distribution of B—B and BBB bonds shown here is one of many that contribute to the "resonance hybrid" ion.*

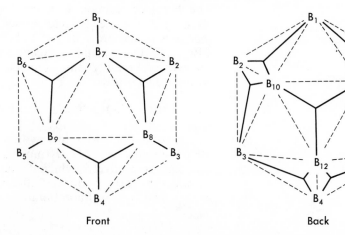

Front   Back

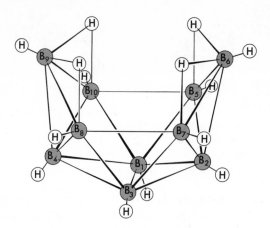

FIGURE 12.5 *Structure of $B_{10}H_{14}$. From W. Lipscomb, Boron Hydrides (New York: W. A. Benjamin, Inc., 1963) Fig. 1-7, p. 7.*

the 1, 2, 3, and 4 positions (using the boron-numbering system of Figs. 12.5 and 12.6), whereas reactions of the latter type yield principally products with the alkyl group in the 6 position.

12.6 HALIDES. The physical properties of the boron trihalides are given in Tables 3.3 and 4.5. Boron trifluoride is formed by heating B_2O_3 with concentrated sulfuric acid and calcium fluoride:

$$B_2O_3 + 3\,H_2SO_4 + 3\,CaF_2 \longrightarrow 2\,BF_3 + 3\,CaSO_4 + 3\,H_2O$$

The other trihalides are prepared by direct combination of the elements at elevated temperatures and by high-temperature halogenation of boric oxide-carbon mixtures:

$$B_2O_3 + 3\,C + 3\,X_2 \longrightarrow 2\,BX_3 + 3\,CO$$

FIGURE 12.6 *A flattened-out skeleton of the $B_{10}H_{14}$ molecule. Every boron atom is bonded to a hydrogen atom not shown. The particular distribution of B—B and BBB bonds shown here is one of several that contribute to the "resonance hybrid" molecule.*

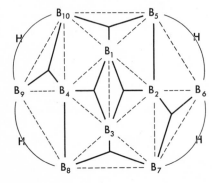

All the trihalides form adducts with strong Lewis bases such as pyridine:

$$BX_3 + \text{base} \longrightarrow \text{base}:BX_3$$

The heats of reaction with pyridine show that the Lewis acid strength increases in the order $BF_3 < BCl_3 < BBr_3$. All the trihalides except the fluoride are rapidly and completely hydrolyzed by water:

$$BX_3 + 3\,H_2O \longrightarrow H_3BO_3 + 3\,H^+ + 3\,X^-$$

Boron trifluoride forms two hydrates, $BF_3 \cdot H_2O$ and $BF_3 \cdot 2\,H_2O$ (mp 10.2° and 6.4°, respectively), which dissolve in water to form boric acid, fluoroborate, and hydroxyfluoroborate:

140

$$4 \, BF_3 + 3 \, H_2O \longrightarrow 3 \, H^+ + 3 \, BF_4^- + H_3BO_3$$

$$BF_4^- + H_2O = BF_3OH^- + HF \qquad K = 2.3 \times 10^{-3}$$

Diboron tetrachloride, B_2Cl_4, is formed when boron trichloride is passed through an electric discharge between mercury electrodes:

$$2 \, BCl_3 + 2 \, Hg \xrightarrow[\text{disch.}]{\text{elec.}} B_2Cl_4 + Hg_2Cl_2$$

The compound is a colorless liquid (fp $-92.6°$, bp $65.5°$) which decomposes on standing at room temperature to a mixture of BCl_3, B_4Cl_4, $B_{12}Cl_{11}$, B_8Cl_8, and $(BCl_{0.6})_x$. The molecule has the structure Cl_2B—BCl_2 and is isoelectronic with the species $C_2O_4^{2-}$ and N_2O_4. The more stable B_2F_4 (mp $-56°$, bp $-34°$) has been prepared by the fluorination of B_2Cl_4 and BO with SbF_3 and SF_4, respectively.

12.7 OXIDES, OXYACIDS, AND BORATES. Boric oxide, B_2O_3, is prepared by the thermal dehydration of **boric acid**, H_3BO_3. The oxide is difficult to crystallize and usually exists as a glass. Boric acid is moderately soluble in water (0.93 M at $25°$); in aqueous solution it is a very weak Lewis acid:

$$B(OH)_3 + H_2O = H^+ + B(OH)_4^- \qquad K_{25°} = 1.05 \times 10^{-9}$$

In boric acid-borate solutions which are more concentrated than about 0.02 M, significant amounts of the **triborate ion**, $B_3O_3(OH)_4^-$, form:

$$2 \, B(OH)_3 + B(OH)_4^- = B_3O_3(OH)_4^- + 3 \, H_2O \qquad K_{25°} = 50$$

At concentrations above $\sim 0.2M$, there is evidence for species such as $B_5O_6(OH)_4^-$, $B_4O_5(OH)_4^{2-}$, and $B_3O_3(OH)_5^{2-}$.

The oxygen chemistry of boron is quite complex. In some borates, the boron atoms are surrounded by three oxygen atoms (trigonal coordination); in other borates, the boron atoms are surrounded by four oxygen atoms (tetrahedral coordination); and in still other borates both trigonal BO_3 groups and tetrahedral BO_4 groups are found. Examples of trigonal coordination are found in the cyclic $B_3O_6^{3-}$ ion of **sodium metaborate** and the infinite chain $(BO_2)_x{}^{x-}$ ion of **calcium metaborate:**

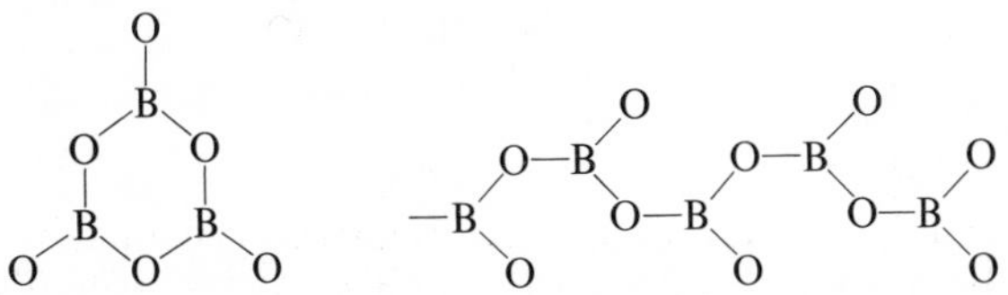

Tetrahedral coordination is found in **boron phosphate**, BPO_4, and **boron arsenate**, $BAsO_4$. The latter compounds are isoelectronic with SiO_2 and have structures analogous to that of the β-cristobalite form of silica. Both types of oxygen coordination are found in the tetraborate ion of **borax,** $Na_2[B_4O_5(OH)_4] \cdot 8\,H_2O$:

$$
\begin{array}{c}
OH \\
| \\
B \\
O \diagup \;\; | \;\; \diagdown O \\
HO-B \quad O \quad B-OH \\
O \diagdown \;\; | \;\; \diagup O \\
B \\
| \\
OH
\end{array}
$$

When borax is dissolved in a large amount of water, the principal reaction is

$$Na_2B_4O_7 \cdot 10\,H_2O \longrightarrow 2\,H_3BO_3 + 2\,Na^+ + 2\,B(OH)_4{}^- + 3\,H_2O$$

Because approximately equimolar amounts of boric acid and borate are formed, the solution is a good buffer and is often used as a pH standard. The pH of $0.01\,M\,Na_2B_2O_7 \cdot 10\,H_2O$ is exactly 9.18 at 25°.

The hydrolysis of B_2Cl_4 yields **$B_2(OH)_4$**, which can be thermally dehydrated to **boron monoxide,** BO. The latter compound also can be prepared by sublimation from a mixture of boron and boric oxide.

12.8 BORON-NITROGEN COMPOUNDS. Boron nitride, BN, is the ultimate product of the pyrolysis of most boron-nitrogen compounds; it can even be made by heating a mixture of boric oxide and ammonium chloride:

$$B_2O_3 + 2\,NH_4Cl \longrightarrow 2\,BN + 3\,H_2O + 2\,HCl$$

When prepared in these ways, boron nitride is a white, slippery solid of density 2.25, having a crystal structure consisting of parallel planes of the following type:

$$
\begin{array}{c}
| \qquad\quad | \\
\diagdown B \diagdown \quad \diagup B \diagdown \\
N \quad N \quad N \\
| \qquad | \qquad | \\
B \quad B \quad B \\
\diagup \quad N \diagup \;\diagdown N \diagdown \\
| \qquad\quad |
\end{array}
$$

Boron nitride is a refractory and relatively chemically inert material. When it is subjected to a pressure of at least 45,000 atm at 1500° or higher, it is converted (in the presence of catalysts) to a cubic form structurally analogous to diamond, having a density of 3.47.

The reactions of the boron trihalides with ammonia are strikingly analogous to the reactions with water. All the trihalides, except BF_3, react with excess ammonia at low temperatures to form boron triamide:

$$BX_3 + 6\,NH_3 \longrightarrow B(NH_2)_3 + 3\,NH_4X$$

The amide slowly loses ammonia at temperatures greater than $0°$ to form $B_2(NH)_3$, and at temperatures above $200°$, deammoniation to BN occurs. BF_3 forms a stable ammoniate, $BF_3 \cdot NH_3$.

When a mixture of lithium borohydride and ammonium chloride is heated to 230–$300°$, **borazine** (the boron-nitrogen analog of benzene) is formed:

$$3\,LiBH_4 + 3\,NH_4Cl \longrightarrow \text{(borazine ring)} + 9\,H_2 + 3\,LiCl$$

Another synthetic method involves the formation of B,B,B-trichloroborazine followed by its reduction to borazine:

$$3\,BCl_3 + 3\,NH_4Cl \longrightarrow \text{(trichloroborazine ring)} + 9\,HCl$$

$$B_3N_3H_3Cl_3 + 3\,NaBH_4 \longrightarrow B_3N_3H_6 + 3\,NaCl + \tfrac{3}{2}\,B_2H_6$$

Resonance structures may be written for borazine, analogous to the Kekulé structures of benzene. As might be expected, borazine has a planar structure. Borazine is a colorless liquid of density 0.86 that freezes at $-58°$ and boils at $55°$. Although borazine's structure and physical properties resemble those of benzene, its chemistry is vastly different. Thus, although benzene is inert toward water and hydrogen chloride under most conditions, borazine undergoes hydrolysis in aqueous solution and readily forms a hydrochloride with HCl:

$$B_3N_3H_6 + 9\,H_2O \longrightarrow 3\,H_3BO_3 + 3\,NH_3 + 3\,H_2$$

$$B_3N_3H_6 + 3\,HCl \longrightarrow \text{(hydrochloride ring)}$$

The difference in reactivity toward these polar reagents is probably due to the polarity of the B—N bond, in contrast to the nonpolar character of the C—C bond.

12.9 ANALYSIS. When a borate or boric acid is warmed with a mixture of concentrated sulfuric acid and a low molecular-weight alcohol such as methanol or ethanol, the corresponding volatile borate ester is formed:

$$H_3BO_3 + 3\,CH_3OH + 3\,H_2SO_4 \longrightarrow B(OCH_3)_3 + 3\,H_3O^+ + 3\,HSO_4^-$$

If the warm alcohol is ignited, the presence of the ester may be detected by the green color imparted to the flame.

Boric acid is such a weak acid in aqueous solutions that it cannot be successfully titrated with base because of the difficulty in determining the endpoint. However, various polyalcohols, especially those with hydroxyl groups on adjacent carbon atoms, react with boric acid to form complexes in the following way:

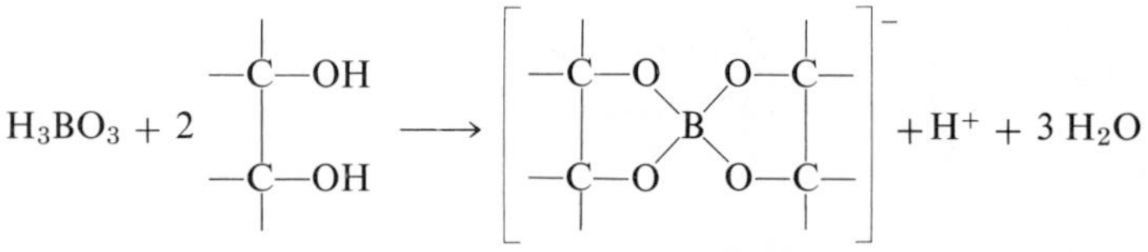

For the case of mannitol, the equilibrium constant is about 10^{-4}; and so, in the presence of mannitol, boric acid may be titrated as a moderately strong acid, using phenolphthalein as indicator.

SUGGESTED REFERENCES

Adams, R. M., ed., *Boron, Metallo-Boron Compounds and Boranes.* New York: Interscience, 1964.

Borax to Boranes, No. 32 in the *Advances in Chemistry Series.* Washington: American Chemical Society, 1961.

Brown, H. C., *Hydroboration.* New York: Benjamin, 1962.

Hawthorne, M. F., "Decaborane-14 and its Derivatives," *Advances in Inorg. Chem. and Radiochem.,* 5, 1963, 307.

Lipscomb, W. N., *Boron Hydrides.* New York: Benjamin, 1963.

Stock, A., *Hydrides of Boron and Silicon.* Ithaca: Cornell University Press, 1933, reissued 1957.

Wells, A. F., *Structural Inorganic Chemistry,* 3rd ed. Oxford: Oxford University Press, 1962.

Index